CANADIAN STORIES

A Cultural Reader for ESL Students

PINETREE SECONDARY ESL

Eleanor Adamowski

Prentice Hall Regents Canada
Don Mills, Ontario

Canadian Cataloguing in Publication Data

Main entry under title:

Canadian stories: a cultural reader for ESL students

ISBN 0-13-288523-9

1. English language — Textbooks for second language learners.* 2. Readers — Canada. 3. Short stories, Canadian (English).* 4. Canadian fiction (English) — 20th century.* I. Adamowski, Eleanor.

PE1128.C35 1993   428.6'4   C93-095481-5

© 1994 Prentice-Hall Canada Inc., Don Mills, Ontario
Pearson Education

Prentice-Hall, Inc., Englewood Cliffs, New Jersey
Prentice-Hall International, Inc., London
Prentice-Hall of Australia, Pty., Ltd., Sydney
Prentice-Hall of India Pvt., Ltd., New Delhi
Prentice-Hall of Japan, Inc., Tokyo
Prentice-Hall of Southeast Asia (Pte.) Ltd., Singapore
Editora Prentice-Hall do Brasil Ltda., Rio de Janeiro
Prentice-Hall Hispanoamericana, S.A., Mexico

ISBN 0-13-288523-9

Acquisitions Editor Joe March
Production Editor Karen Frances Sacks
Production Coordinator Anita Boyle
Cover design Olena Serbyn

23456789 DMP 05432
Printed and bound in Canada

Contents

SUMMARY QUESTIONS

Map of Canada

Acknowledgements

I am grateful to many people for their help in realizing this project. First of all, sincere appreciation for the extensive help of Wang Wenxia and the support of St. Mary's University (Halifax) Canada/China Language and Cultural Program for a cultural module on short Canadian fiction which led to this text. I am indebted to the visiting Chinese scholars who were enthusiastic to discuss culture.

Special thanks to Trudy Kennell and Rebecca Adamowski for suggesting and reading many stories for this text and giving helpful criticism, and to Wang Wenxia, Betty Armstrong, and Elizabeth Taborek for their support and suggestions.

Many thanks to Jura Seskus for using parts of the final manuscript and making many helpful suggestions.

I am also very much indebted to Marc Enkin of Village Studio for the production of the tapes of the stories, and to readers David Collins, Chris Gudgeon, Ace Silver, Patrick Tierney, and Xiaolei Wu.

Finally, I would like to thank my editor, Karen Sacks, at Prentice Hall Canada for all her help, as well as the anonymous reviewers who gave invaluable suggestions.

Grateful acknowledgement is made to the following for permission to reprint the selections in this volume:

"Penny in the Dust" from *Rebellion of Young David* by Ernest Buckler, used by permission of the Canadian Publishers, McClelland & Stewart, Toronto.

"A Secret Lost in the Water" from *The Hockey Sweater and Other Stories* by Roch Carrier, trans. by Sheila Fischman, (c) 1979; The House of Anansi Press Ltd., reprinted by permission of Stoddart Publishing Company Ltd., Don Mills, Ont.

"The Torch Woman" from *Wild Drums: Tales and Legends of the Plains Indians* as told to Nan Shipley by Alex Grisdale, Winnipeg: Peguis Publishers, 1974; reprinted by permission.

"The Dead Child" from *Enchanted Summer* by Gabrielle Roy (Joyce Marshall, trans.), (c) Fonds Gabrielle Roy.

"Lies My Father Told Me" by Ted Allan, reprinted with permission of the author.

"The Other Family" by Himani Bannerji; reprinted with the permission of the author.

"Shun-Wai" by Taien Ng, reprinted with the permission of the author.

"The Moose and the Sparrow" from *Men and Women* by Hugh Garner, (c) Hugh Garner.

"Lifeguard" by Barbara Scott, reprinted by permission of the author.

"Food and Spirits" from *Food and Spirits* by Beth Brant (co-published by Press Gang Publications and Firebrand Books, Ithaca, New York, 1991), reprinted with permission of the author.

Preface to the Student

Canadian Stories: A Cultural Reader for ESL Students is a collection of short stories for high-intermediate and advanced English as a second or foreign language adult students. Its purpose is to further develop your reading skills and your enjoyment of Canadian short stories. As a cultural reader, it also aims to encourage an exploration of culture—the culture of each reader and the culture of Canada.

The stories in this reader are about relationships in families and among friends. They open a "window" on life in Canada. Some are set in a Canada of earlier times, written by English, French and native Canadians. Others show Canada in recent times, by writers of varying ethnic origins who offer a glimpse of the variety of attitudes and feelings which co-exist in multicultural Canada.

WHY A CULTURAL READER?

Language and culture are closely linked. Knowing what various people in Canada value can help you understand why people act as they do. This will make you more comfortable when you interact with Canadians and aid in your facility with the language.

You may wonder why you should be reading fiction. Why not read about "real" people? You probably are reading Canadian newspaper and magazine articles. Fiction, however, is a special kind of prose which can involve us in a way that makes us feel we are sharing an experience with the people (characters) in the story. The fiction of another culture can show us what is important to the people in that society while it clarifies for us what we ourselves really care about.

When we read about characters in a work of fiction, we not only see them through the eyes of the writer but also through our own eyes. We bring our own experiences to the story and interpret events in our own way. For example, if the story is about a mother or a friend, these words have a personal meaning for us individually. Words are part of culture. Anthropologists define culture as the patterns of beliefs and behaviours of groups (the way we eat, sleep, and feel about things). We share a culture with those who grew up with us. But we each have our own "culture" as well: sisters and brothers often have different views and habits even though they are part of one family.

As you clarify what is most important to you, you may be asked to tell your own story to the others in your class. Not all cultures in Canada can be represented in this text, and your own values and customs are just as important. Therefore, if the "window" on *your* life opens during class discussions, the picture of Canadian life emerging will be more complete.

WHAT ABOUT LANGUAGE SKILLS?

While you concentrate on reading and understanding fiction, you will develop reading skills and increase your vocabulary. In addition, discussing the stories will help with speaking and listening skills. These skills carry over to non-fiction reading and everyday communication with speakers of English. You can also gain the independence to read materials on a wide variety of topics and more complicated literature such as novels and poetry.

HOW TO USE THIS TEXT

Each story is preceded by information about the author and prereading questions to prepare you for the theme or topic of the selection. The questions should be answered from your own experience and the answers explored with others so that you begin with a curiosity which you want the story to satisfy.

Read the story for pleasure, as quickly as you can, trying to understand the general idea. On first reading, do not worry about words you do not recognize unless they prevent you from understanding what is happening. (Remember that when you learned to read your first language, you probably did not use a dictionary and yet you still grew in your ability to read and develop a large vocabulary.) If you need help, however, you can glance at the short definitions of words at the end of the story. List the words you do not understand and look at them more closely later on.

The *Closer Reading* questions require that you skim, scan, summarize, explain, or read between the lines—reading skills which will ensure your ability to read English at an advanced level. The *Cultural Discussion* questions are important for understanding the full meaning of the stories. They require you to think and talk about your own culture and ask questions of others. Instructors will share their perceptions as well, but remember that these perceptions may sometimes be different from those of other Canadians. One instructor cannot be "Canada".

The sections called *Looking at Language* and *Reinforcing Skills* look specifically at some of the language in each selection and help you to develop strategies for finding word and phrase meaning on your own, outside of a classroom. The activities at the end of each chapter include opportunities to tell your own stories and provide essay topics for those who want to work on essay writing skills.

OBJECTIVES

1. To enjoy reading so that you read more and learn the language by seeing it in context.
2. To develop strategies that increase reading fluency and the ability to figure out the meaning of new words and phrases within a story.
3. To learn about life in Canada and the attitudes of individual people as suggested in the stories.
4. To develop awareness of your own culture so that you can become a teacher as well as a learner.
5. To practice the speaking and listening skills of discussion so that you will be confident interacting with English speakers.

Preface to the Instructor

Learning a language for communication necessitates learning about how a culture works. Literature has traditionally been the means most often used to show how human beings think and feel about life. The stories in this cultural reader have been carefully chosen for their portrayal of the lives of French and English descendants, native people, and more recent European and non-European immigrants. Most of the stories are set in various parts of Canada at various times beginning just before the 1920s. They do not try to give the newcomer an all-encompassing picture but rather some idea of the traditions and values of some people they will meet here. The students themselves will contribute insights from their own cultures to round out the story of Canadian life. The theme of family and friends ensures that every reader will have a point of reference and, through reading and discussion, feel more confident in his or her ability to communicate in English.

THE TEXT AND ITS USE

Each story is accompanied by information about the author, prereading focus questions and a glossary to help high-intermediate and advanced ESL readers get through the story as quickly as possible. *A Closer Reading* guides the student's second reading and helps the instructor gauge comprehension as students skim, scan, summarize, explain, and compare while recounting events, describing characters, analyzing motives, and thinking about meaning. In other words, while the students focus on content, they quite naturally practice skills such as reading between the lines which reading authentic literature requires. The *Cultural Discussion* questions encourage readers to think about the attitudes portrayed in each story and to articulate their own beliefs and values.

The section *Looking at Language* examines the elements and organization of short stories as well as reading strategies. This helps students become independent readers—of both literary and non-literary texts. The *Activities* section includes student storytelling which gives them the opportunity to share their experiences and increase speaking fluency. Essay topics are also offered for students who need or want to work on essay writing. *Reinforcing Skills* encourages students to practice skills further by applying them to another story.

The supplemental audio tape of the readings is a tool for helping students enjoy and understand the stories while improving their listening skills. The readers trace their roots back to countries as diverse as China, Russia, and Jamaica, giving students a chance to hear different voices and authentic speech. The tape can be played independently in a language lab as well as in a classroom. The dialogues can be springboards for pronunciation practice of rhythm and stress and can lead to dramatic readings by the students.

The Instructor's Guide gives additional background about the literature and provides teaching suggestions and follow-up activities. It can give confidence to a teacher who finds teaching Canadian stories a new and interesting idea.

THE STORIES

The stories were chosen for their readability; that is, stories that can be enjoyed by learners of different backgrounds, ages, and experiences. All of the stories have a clear plot and are realistic (as opposed to post-modern or experimental) on the principle that they can be read without too much difficulty. They are still richly complex and encourage deeper explorations once students achieve a basic idea of what is happening in the stories.

Although this text would provide a good introduction for students planning to take a non-ESL university English course, the emphasis is on cultural analysis and language learning strategies rather than literary analysis. Students who wish to pursue science or technical studies will become equally involved in the stories and discussion, becoming more accomplished readers with the cultural knowledge necessary to function in an English-speaking society.

The stories in **Part I: Legacies** show a pre-1950s Canada of small villages, farms and neighbourhoods. The legacies are memories and skills that have meant a lot to the narrators. "Penny in the Dust" recalls rural Nova Scotia just before the 1920s. "A Secret Lost in the Water" is set in rural Quebec in the 1940s, while "The Dead Child" remembers a Métis village of Manitoba in the late 1920s. "Lies My Father Told Me" takes place in a Jewish neighbourhood in Montreal sometime in the 1920s. All these stories are concerned with family and community, questions about how individual differences can be reconciled, how children can be taught what is important, and how people share feelings of love and respect. "The Torch Woman" tells a very old tale about an Indian widow whose bravery and cleverness made her a heroine in times before Columbus: a legacy of North American culture quite different from that of European descendants.

There were also many new immigrants to Canada during the first part of the twentieth century who were not from Great Britain or France, but Canadian literature as a whole, and especially Canadian short stories, did not often reflect their existence. In **Legacies** students will see if they have anything in common with these earlier immigrants.

The time period of **Part II: Adaptations** extends from the 1960s to the present, when multiculturalism was becoming the policy as well as the reality in

Canada. The stories therefore reflect the reality of many cultures living together, and the many kinds of adaptations required in times of rapid change. "The Other Family" concerns a child whose skin is brown in a culture which seems to expect it to be white. In "Shun-Wai" a young woman of Chinese descent searches for her identity and observes some ironic differences within her own family. "Lifeguard" is about a newly independent sixteen-year-old boy who has responsibility for a younger boy thrust upon him (the realistic language includes "four-letter words"). "The Moose and the Sparrow", an old-fashioned action story about how one young man reacts to a difficult new environment, ends with a dark twist. This section closes with "Food and Spirits", a recent story about an Indian grandfather who travels from the reserve to the big city with unexpected effects on the "other culture" he encounters.

WHAT IS CANADIAN CULTURE?

The question "whose culture do we teach?" implies that one approach or one text can or will teach all about a culture. Of course it will not. Each story shows one small part of the experiences that make up life here. The goal is not to reveal Canada, but to explore the views in the stories and those of the students, to see where their feelings meet and where they go separate ways. No consensus need be reached. The awareness of multiple impressions may be intimidating at first but it can lead to a confidence which will allow students to become more active participants in Canadian life.

PART I

LEGACIES

Life in Canada between World War I and World War II was quite different from the way you see it now. Although the size of the cities was rapidly growing, many people still lived on farms. Writers tended to portray Canada as a country of small towns and villages with traditional values centred on family and community. As you can see from some of the stories, life was a struggle for people who lived in rural areas.

The first two stories are about English- and French-speaking immigrants. Until recent times, these people were the majority of Canada's immigrants but by the late nineteenth century, many thousands of immigrants were coming to Canada who spoke neither French nor English. The story by Ted Allan is about Jewish immigrants who came to Canada from Russia probably sometime after 1881.

When the French and the English arrived, the native peoples had already been here for thousands of years. "The Torch Woman" is set in pre-Columbian times. The children in "The Dead Child" are Métis from the late 1920s, the descendants of native people and French explorers and settlers, studying in the French language.

These stories tell about legacies (gifts from the past) which are part of Canadian culture. Are they at all similar to your legacies?

PENNY IN THE DUST
ERNEST BUCKLER
(1908-1984)

Ernest Buckler is a writer from Nova Scotia who did a graduate degree in philosophy at the University of Toronto and five years later returned home to be a farmer. Sometimes autobiographical (about his own life), Buckler's lyrical stories show families that are close, if not always compatible. Life in Buckler's stories has its wonderful moments and its tragedies. His best-known book, The Mountain and the Valley *(1952), is about the life of a sensitive, artistic young man. "Penny in the Dust" is from* The Rebellion of Young David *(1975), a book of short stories written over many years.*

PREPARING TO READ

This story is about a poor farming family in rural Nova Scotia in the time of Buckler's boyhood, probably around 1916. Canada was at war from 1914-1918. Even before the war, the Maritime provinces had suffered from changing demands for their traditional fish, timber, and shipbuilding industries. Even in good times, farming has usually been a precarious (risky) way of making a living in Canada. What do you suppose life was like for a farming family such as this one?

In "Penny in the Dust" a boy named Peter is talking with his sister after their father has died, and they recall something that happened when Peter was a seven-year-old boy on the farm. The son thinks again about his relationship with his father and changes his idea of what his father was like. Do you think we really know the people we live with? Do all people express their feelings openly?

If you have difficulty with the language in this story, turn to the *Glossary* and *Looking at Language* at the end of the story for help.

My sister and I were walking through the old sun-still fields the evening before my father's funeral, recalling this memory or that—trying, after the fashion of families who gather again in the place where they were born, to identify ourselves with the strange children we must have been.

"Do you remember the afternoon we thought you were lost?" my sister said. I did. That was as long ago as the day I was seven, but I'd had occasion to remember it only yesterday.

"We searched everywhere," she said, "Up in the meetinghouse, back in the blueberry barrens—we even looked in the well. I think it's the only time I ever saw Father really upset. He didn't even stop to take the oxen off the wagon tongue when they told him. He raced right through the chopping where Tom Reeve was burning brush, looking for you—right through the flames almost; they couldn't do a thing with him. And you up in your bed, sound asleep!

"It was all over losing a penny or something, wasn't it?" she went on, when I didn't answer. It was. She laughed indulgently. "You were a crazy kid, weren't you."

I was. But there was more to it than that. I had never seen a shining new penny before that day. I'd thought they were all black. This one was bright as gold. And my father had given it to me.

You would have to understand about my father, and that is the hard thing to tell. If I say that he worked all day long but never once had I seen him hurry, that would make him sound like a stupid man. If I say that he never held me on his knee when I was a child and that I never heard him laugh out loud in his life, it would make him sound humourless and severe. If I said that whenever I'd be reeling off some of my fanciful plans and he'd come into the kitchen and I'd stop short, you'd think that he was distant and that in some kind of way I was afraid of him. None of that would be true.

There's no way you can tell it to make it sound like anything more than an inarticulate man a little at sea with an imaginative child. You'll have to take my word for it that there was more to it than that. It was as if his sure-footed way in the fields forsook him the moment he came near the door of my child's world and that he could never intrude on it without feeling awkward and conscious of trespass; and that I, sensing that but not understanding it, felt at the sound of his solid step outside, the child-world's foolish fragility. He would fix the small spot where I planted beans and other quick-sprouting seeds before he prepared the big garden, even if the spring was late; but he wouldn't ask me how many rows I wanted and if he made three rows and I wanted four, I couldn't ask him to change them. If I walked behind the load of hay, longing to ride, and he walked ahead of the oxen, I couldn't ask him to put me up and he wouldn't make any move to do so until he saw me trying to grasp the binder.

He, my father, had just given me a new penny, bright as gold.

He'd taken it from his pocket several times, pretending to examine the date on it, waiting for me to notice it. He couldn't offer me *anything* until I had shown some sign that the gift would be welcome.

"You can have it if you want it, Pete," he said at last.

"Oh, thanks," I said. Nothing more. I couldn't expose any of my eagerness either.

I started with it, to the store. For a penny you could buy the magic cylinder of "Long Tom" popcorn with Heaven knows what glittering bauble inside. But the more I thought of my bright penny disappearing forever into the black drawstring pouch the storekeeper kept his money in, the slower my steps lagged as the store came nearer and nearer. I sat down in the road.

It was that time of magic suspension in an August afternoon. The lifting smells of leaves and cut clover hung still in the sun. The sun drowsed, like a kitten curled up on my shoulder. The deep flour-fine dust in the road puffed about my bare ankles, warm and soft as sleep. The sound of the cowbells came sharp and hollow from the cool swamp.

I began to play with the penny, putting off the decision. I would close my eyes and bury it deep in the sand; and then, with my eyes still closed, get up and walk around, and then come back to search for it. Tantalizing myself, each time, with the excitement of discovering afresh its bright shining edge. I did that again and again. Alas, once too often.

It was almost dark when their excited talking in the room awakened me. It was Mother who had found me. I suppose when it came dusk she thought of me in my bed other nights, and I suppose she looked there without any reasonable hope but only as you look in every place where the thing that is lost has ever lain before. And now suddenly she was crying because when she opened the door there, miraculously, I was.

"Peter!" she cried, ignoring the obvious in her sudden relief, "*where* have you been?"

"I lost my penny," I said.

"You lost your penny...? But what made you come up here and hide?"

If Father hadn't been there, I might have told her the whole story. But when I looked up at Father, standing there like the shape of everything sound and straight, it was like daylight shredding the memory of a silly dream. How could I bear the shame of repeating before him the childish visions I had built in my head in the magic August afternoon when almost anything could be made to seem real, as I buried the penny and dug it up again? How could I explain that pit-of-the-stomach sickness which struck through the whole day when I had to believe, at last, that it was really gone? How could I explain that I wasn't really hiding from *them*? How, with the words and the understanding I had then, that this was the only possible place to run from that awful feeling of loss?

"I lost my penny," I said again. I looked at Father and turned my face into the pillow. "I want to go to sleep."

"Peter," Mother said. "It's almost nine o'clock. You haven't had a bite of supper. Do you know you almost scared the *life* out of us?"

"You better get some supper," Father said. It was the only time he had spoken.

I never dreamed that he would mention the thing again. But the next morning when we had the hay forks in our hands, ready to toss out the clover, he seemed to postpone the moment of actually leaving for the field. He stuck his fork in the ground and brought in another pail of water, though the kettle was chock full. He took out the shingle nail that held a broken yoke strap together and put it back in exactly the same hole. He went into the shed to see if the pigs had cleaned up all their breakfast.

And then he said abruptly: "Ain't you got no idea where you lost your penny?"

"Yes," I said, "I know just about."

"Let's see if we can't find it," he said.

We walked down the road together, stiff with awareness. He didn't hold my hand.

"It's right here somewhere," I said. "I was playin' with it, in the dust."

He looked at me, but he didn't ask me what game anyone could possibly play with a penny in the dust.

I might have known he would find it. He could tap the alder bark with his jackknife just exactly hard enough so it wouldn't split but so it would twist free from the notched wood, to make a whistle. His great fingers could trace loose the hopeless snarl of a fishing line that I could only succeed in tangling tighter and tighter. If I broke the handle of my wheelbarrow ragged beyond sight of any possible repair, he could take it and bring it back to me so you could hardly see the splice if you weren't looking for it.

He got down on his knees and drew his fingers carefully through the dust, like a harrow; not clawing it frantically into heaps as I had done, covering even as I uncovered. He found the penny almost at once.

He held it in his hand, as if the moment of passing it to me were a deadline for something he dreaded to say, but must. Something that could not be put off any longer, if it were to be spoken at all.

"Pete," he said, "you needn'ta hid. I wouldn'ta beat you."

Beat me? Oh, Father! You didn't think that was the reason...? I felt almost sick. I felt as if I had struck *him*.

I had to tell him the truth then. Because only the truth, no matter how ridiculous it was, would have the unmistakable sound truth has, to scatter that awful idea out of his head.

"I wasn't hidin', Father," I said, "honest. I was... I was buryin' my penny and makin' out I was diggin' up treasure. I was makin' out I was findin' gold. I didn't know what to *do* when I lost it, I just didn't know where to *go*...." His head was bent forward, like mere listening. I had to make it truer still.

"I made out it was gold," I said desperately, "and I—I was makin' out I bought you a mowin' machine so's you could get your work done early every day so's you and I could go in to town in the big automobile I made out I bought you—and everyone'd turn around and look at us drivin' down the streets...." His head was perfectly still, as if he were only waiting with patience for me to finish. "*Laugh*in' and *talk*in'," I said. Louder, smiling intensely, com*pell*ing him, by the absolute conviction of some true particular, to believe me.

He looked up then. It was the only time I had ever seen tears in his eyes. It was the only time in my seven years that he had ever put his arm around me.

I wondered, though, why he hesitated, and then put the penny back in his own pocket.

Yesterday I knew. I never found any fortune and we never had a car to ride in together. But I think he knew what that would be like, just the same. I found the penny again yesterday, when we were getting out his good suit—in an upper vest pocket where no one ever carries change. It was still shining. He must have kept it polished.

I left it there.

GLOSSARY

alder bark   the outside of a tree
at sea   confused
barrens   land not suitable for growing things
binder   a machine that cuts and ties grain
chopping   area where wood is cut up
compelling   forcing
conscious of trespass   knowing he did not belong there
cylinder   long, rounded container
forsook   abandoned
glittering bauble   attractive but worthless object
harrow   a farm tool
indulgently   forgiving his foolishness
lagged   got slower
needn'ta   need not have (did not need to)
notched   a V-shaped cut
reeling off   telling many long stories
sun-still   as the sun goes down, the land is still
suspension   stopping for awhile
tantalizing   teasing
to identify ourselves   to see ourselves

tongue   the part of a wagon that attaches it to the oxen or horse
wouldn'ta   would not have

A CLOSER READING

1. The narrator's sister reminds the protagonist of an event that happened when he was seven years old. What happened? Why does she remember it now?

2. Peter had lost a penny. What was its value (in this story)?

3. What was his father like? Did the way he acted have anything to do with Peter's own personality? What was Peter like?

4. Why did Peter put off spending the penny? Does his behaviour seem strange to you?

5. What does *"Alas, once too often"* mean?

6. The story jumps from Peter's playing with the penny to his seeming to hide in his room. How do we know what has happened? What is the mother's reaction to finding him? The father's?

7. How does the father act on the following day? What is his difficulty?

8. What effect does Peter's view of his father's abilities have on Peter?

9. Why is the father affected so much by Peter's explanation? Why does he keep the penny for himself?

10. Why does Peter leave the penny in his father's coat pocket?

11. Do you think the father and son had a smooth relationship after this episode?

CULTURAL DISCUSSION

1. What is your image of a good father? A good son?

2. What kind of problems do fathers and sons or mothers and daughters have? Does this depend on the country and culture? Are there "universals" (things that are true the world over)?

3. Did this story remind you of anyone you know? Was there any event in your childhood which you will always remember? Is it something you can talk about, or are such memories private?

4. The first three stories in this text are about the experiences of young boys. Would the stories be different if they were about young girls?

5. If the life of a farmer was so difficult, why do you suppose Buckler returned to the farm after he received a graduate degree in philosophy?

LOOKING AT LANGUAGE

Talking About Short Stories

Terms

Like all traditional short stories in the Western tradition, "Penny in the Dust" has a *setting* (a farm in Nova Scotia around 1916), *characters* (Peter, his sister, his father, his mother), a *narrator* who tells the story (Peter, as a man), and a *plot* (what happens). We talk about stories using these terms.

Some of the vocabulary in this story may be unfamiliar. If you understand the plot, the vocabulary will become easier to figure out. What is the plot of this story? (Tell what happens in your own words.)

The main idea

Sometimes the first paragraph of a story has so many unfamiliar words that it is difficult to understand the main idea. In this case, try reading past the difficult words and concentrating on the nouns, pronouns, verbs and prepositions you recognize. In this way, the first paragraph of "Penny" might read like this:

> My sister and I walking through fields evening before father's funeral, memory.

These words will give you the main idea of the paragraph. Try to string together the key words you recognize in the third paragraph of "Penny".

Paraphrase

The paragraph rewritten in your own words is called a *paraphrase*. Paraphrasing means saying or writing a passage in other words, keeping the most important ideas. It is a useful skill for reading non-fiction as well as fiction.

Style

Reread the passages in which you listed difficult words in order to understand the meaning of those words. You can see how the writer uses words to create a mood and draw us into the story. Buckler has a lyrical style; that is, he tries to show how the narrator really feels as he tells us his emotion-filled story. Do you think Buckler succeeds in this goal?

How does Buckler's style work? First, he uses many adjectives to describe what the farm and land look like. The hyphenated words such as *sun-still, sure-footed, quick-sprouting,* and *flour-fine* give the story a home-made flavour. The realistic description of farm tools reminds us that this is a story about rural life in an earlier time. Also, he uses some long sentences with several clauses and *and*s. For example:

If I said that/ whenever I'd be reeling off some of my fanciful plans/
and he'd come into the kitchen/ and I'd stop short,/ you'd think that
he was distant/ and in some kind of way I was afraid of him.

This kind of writing sounds like someone who is having trouble explaining something (which he is). The relationship between the father and son is awkward; the
prose style shows that difficulty.

When you read Roch Carrier's story, you will see a very different style of writing and can compare the two styles.

Dialogue

Did the characters in Buckler's story sound like real people talking? The characters
are farmers and their speech is informal, for example, *"Ain't you got no idea where
you lost your penny?"*. Good writers have an ear for natural-sounding dialogue.

ACTIVITIES

Essay Writing

1. Write a long paragraph telling what happened in the story, in sequence (first,
   then/next, finally). Begin with Peter getting the penny.
2. Write a short essay comparing/contrasting Peter and his father. Be sure to
   include evidence from the text.

A SECRET LOST IN THE WATER

ROCH CARRIER
(b. 1937)

Translated by Sheila Fischman

Roch Carrier was born in Quebec, received an M.A. from the University of Montreal, and a doctorate from the Sorbonne. He taught at the University of Montreal and has written many novels, stories, plays and poetry, all translated into English and other languages. He is one of Canada's most famous writers. This short story is from The Hockey Sweater and Other Stories *(1979). His latest novel is* The Man in the Closet *(1993).*

PREPARING TO READ

This is a story about a writer who returns to his boyhood village and is reminded of something his father taught him in his early childhood, perhaps in the 1940s. It is set in rural Quebec during the time (before the 1960s) when land was one of the most important values, along with family, community, and pastoral (rural) life.

What do you think education in Quebec was like in the 1940s? Was everyone educated in schools? What results when one generation learns from experience and the next one learns from books? Which is the better teacher: books or experience?

After I started going to school my father scarcely talked any more. I was very intoxicated by the new game of spelling; my father had little skill for it (it was my mother who wrote our letters) and was convinced I was no longer interested in hearing him tell of his adventures during the long weeks when he was far away from the house.

One day, however, he said to me:

'The time's come to show you something.'

He asked me to follow him. I walked behind him, not talking, as we had got in the habit of doing. He stopped in the field before a clump of leafy bushes.

'Those are called alders,' he said.

'I know.'

'You have to learn how to choose,' my father pointed out.

I didn't understand. He touched each branch of the bush, one at a time, with religious care.

'You have to choose one that's very fine, a perfect one, like this.'

I looked; it seemed exactly like the others.

My father opened his pocket knife and cut the branch he'd selected with pious care. He stripped off the leaves and showed me the branch, which formed a perfect Y.

'You see,' he said, 'the branch has two arms. Now take one in each hand. And squeeze them.'

I did as he asked and took in each hand one fork of the Y, which was thinner than a pencil.

'Close your eyes,' my father ordered, 'and squeeze a little harder... Don't open your eyes! Do you feel anything?'

'The branch is moving!' I exclaimed, astonished.

Beneath my clenched fingers the alder was wriggling like a small, frightened snake. My father saw that I was about to drop it.

'Hang on to it!'

'The branch is squirming,' I repeated. 'And I hear something that sounds like a river!'

'Open your eyes,' my father ordered.

I was stunned, as though he'd awakened me while I was dreaming.

'What does it mean?' I asked my father.

'It means that underneath us, right here, there's a little freshwater spring. If we dig, we could drink from it. I've just taught you how to find a spring. It's something my own father taught me. It isn't something you learn in school. And it isn't useless: a man can get along without writing and arithmetic, but he can never get along without water.

Much later, I discovered that my father was famous in the region because of what the people called his 'gift': before digging a well they always consulted him; they would watch him prospecting the fields or the hills, eyes closed, hands clenched on the fork of an alder bough. Wherever my father stopped, they marked the ground; there they would dig; and from there water would gush forth.

Years passed; I went to other schools, saw other countries, I had children, I wrote some books and my poor father is lying in the earth where so many times he had found fresh water.

One day someone began to make a film about my village and its inhabitants, from whom I've stolen so many of the stories that I tell. With the film crew we went to see a farmer to capture the image of a sad man: his children didn't want to receive the inheritance he'd spent his whole life preparing for them—the finest farm in the area. While the technicians were getting cameras and microphones ready the farmer put his arm around my shoulders, saying:

'I knew your father well.'

'Ah! I know. Everybody in the village knows each other... No one feels like an outsider.'

'You know what's under your feet?'

'Hell?' I asked, laughing.

'Under your feet there's a well. Before I dug I called in specialists from the Department of Agriculture; they did research, they analyzed shovelfuls of dirt; and they made a report where they said there wasn't any water on my land. With the family, the animals, the crops, I need water. When I saw that those specialists hadn't found any I thought of your father and I asked him to come over. He didn't want to; I think he was pretty fed up with me because I'd asked those specialists instead of him. But finally he came; he went and cut off a little branch, then he walked around for a while with his eyes shut; he stopped, he listened to something we couldn't hear and then he said to me: "Dig right here, there's enough water to get your whole flock drunk and drown your specialists besides." We dug and found water. Fine water that's never heard of pollution.'

The film people were ready; they called to me to take my place.

'I'm gonna show you something,' said the farmer, keeping me back. 'You wait right here.'

He disappeared into a shack which he must have used to store things, then came back with a branch which he held out to me.

'I never throw nothing away; I kept the alder branch your father cut to find my water. I don't understand, it hasn't dried out.'

Moved as I touched the branch, kept out of I don't know what sense of piety— and which really wasn't dry—I had the feeling that my father was watching me over my shoulder; I closed my eyes and, standing above the spring my father had discovered, I waited for the branch to writhe. I hoped the sound of gushing water would rise to my ears.

The alder stayed motionless in my hands and the water beneath the earth refused to sing.

Somewhere along the roads I'd taken since the village of my childhood I had forgotten my father's knowledge.

'Don't feel sorry,' said the man, thinking no doubt of his farm and his childhood; 'nowadays fathers can't pass on anything to the next generation.'

And he took the alder branch from my hands.

GLOSSARY

alders   trees or shrubs of the birch family growing in moist ground
hell   (*religious*) a place of torment where sinners go after death
intoxicated   excited
moved   (I was moved) my emotions were stirred
pious   very respectful
prospecting   exploring for minerals
spring   a source of water in the ground
squirming   twisting about like a worm
to sing   (*poetic*) to make a sound
writhe   squirm

A CLOSER READING

1. What happened when the boy went to school? Why?

2. What is his father's special skill? What does the father wish to teach his son?

3. What does *"stolen so many stories"* mean?

4. What does the son discover when he returns to his village after he has become a famous writer? Why can't he get the branch to move?

5. What does the farmer mean in the sentence that begins *"Nowadays..."* at the end of the story?

6. How do you think the narrator feels when the farmer takes the alder branch from his hands?

CULTURAL DISCUSSION

1. Most parents want to teach their children the skills they need for life. Is this true in the country where you grew up? What skills were most important?

2. *"No one feels like an outsider."* Does this apply to the place where you grew up? To the place you live now?

3. What do you think of the son? What do you think others in Canada would think of him?

4. Do you agree with the farmer when he says *"Nowadays..."* at the end of the story?
5. What life skills did you learn from your parents?
6. What skills do you wish to pass on to your children? Does moving to another country make it difficult to pass on traditions?

LOOKING AT LANGUAGE

Outlining a Short Story

A traditional short story includes setting, plot, and character (as discussed after "Penny in the Dust"). There is usually a conflict or problem, *climax* (a high point or turning point), and finally a conclusion. Outlining the parts of a story can be helpful in understanding it. Outline "A Secret Lost in the Water" using these terms:

a. setting
b. character(s)
c. plot
d. climax
e. conclusion

If you were writing a story about some event in your youth, how would you outline it? Use the terms above as a guide.

REINFORCING SKILLS

Writers have different styles of writing. Note the following about Carrier's style:

- unusual punctuation (many colons and semi-colons)
- a "spare" style, one with few adjectives
- a lot of time and information is covered in the two sentences of the first paragraph
- characters speak very clearly and directly
- the whole story takes a very short time to tell

Compare Carrier's style in this story to Buckler's in "Penny in the Dust". Both stories take place on farms, but Buckler uses many adjectives, repeats phrases, and writes long, complicated sentences. If you read these two stories out loud, which one moves faster? Which one slows us down? Which one is more emotional? Which one do you prefer?

The dialogue in a story is important: the words the characters speak show us what they are like, as well as help to tell the story. Notice that the father in the story repeats *"You have to"* and *"You see"* and gives orders when he talks. What does this tell us about him and his concerns? Is he anything like the father in "Penny in the

Dust"? Is the son in "A Secret Lost in the Water" anything like the son in "Penny"? (Hint: look at what they say.)

ACTIVITIES

Oral

Tell a story about your own education, either in school or through experience. Narrow your topic down to one particular skill you learned. Write an outline first to help you organize the story.

Essay Writing

1. Write a paragraph in sequence telling what happens in this story (in your own words): first, then/next, finally.

2. Write a short essay arguing the topic: Which is better: learning by experience or learning by books?

THE TORCH WOMAN
BY ALEX GRISDALE
(1875-1973)

Alex Grisdale was from the Brokenhead Reserve in Manitoba. As a young man he listened to his father's stories and wrote down 800 of them. They were lost in a fire at a mission, but he wrote them again. He told them to Nan Shipley who translated them word-for-word and, in 1974, some of them, including "The Torch Woman", were published as Wild Drums: Tales and Legends of the Plains Indians.

PREPARING TO READ

The native peoples' traditional literatures are oral ones which include myths, legends, songs and prayers handed down by word of mouth from generation to generation. The purpose of the literature was to pass on the culture and its values. In the past, anthropologists and other interested people helped to write some of this oral literature in English. Now native people are making a concerted effort to put their oral heritage into written English and to include journals and autobiographies as well as new stories and novels.

Myths are stories about the beginnings of a nation or a religion, its gods and its heroes. A legend tells of heroic acts that serve as examples to people through the ages. Although short stories were not part of traditional native story telling, native writers are now combining Western literary techniques with their own myths and legends to produce stories for native and non-native readers which reflect their culture.

"The Torch Woman" is a tale passed down orally, set in a time when the Assiniboine and the Sioux were at war, before the European migration in the sixteenth century. Do you know anything about the cultures of the native peoples before 1492? After 1492? Many Canadians and Americans have now begun to take strong interest in the people who were the first inhabitants of the North and South American continents.

This story concerns a young widow. What image does a "young widow" bring to mind? What role have widows played in different countries? What about "warriors"? Can women be warriors? Indian stories tell about women who fought bravely for their people. Are warrior women part of your cultural heritage?

Many years before the white man came to this country a band of Indians set up their tepees by the Assiniboine River near where Brandon city now stands. These were Stone Roasters, people who dropped hot roasted stones into water to make it boil. This tribe is now called the Assiniboine. The band made their camp near a cut bank where the land dropped fifteen or sixteen feet over the rocks into the water. The chief chose this safe place because enemies could not approach by river.

There was a widow in this camp, and because she was young and childless she was expected to look after herself. Her husband had been killed by the Sioux and she was still in mourning for him when the scouts rode in to report a large herd of buffalo about a day's ride out on the plains. At once the people prepared to break camp and move closer to the hunt.

"I will remain here until you return," the widow said.

Her friends were alarmed. "What will you do if the enemy comes while you are alone? We will be gone for the days of one hand."

She shrugged and continued to scrape fat from a buffalo hide with her sharp flint stone scraper. "If this happens then I shall surely die."

When the chief saw that the woman was determined to remain in her tepee by the river, he ordered that three other lodges remain standing. This might deceive any spies into believing several families were here instead of a lone woman.

The people rode away to the buffalo hunt and the widow slept one night without fear. Only the sound of the river and far away coyotes disturbed the dark stillness. But she knew that if enemy scouts were about and had seen the departure of the band they would lie patiently watching the four tepees to count the men who went in and out. It would not be long before they would discover that she was alone. But she was prepared to die, for her husband had been dead two moons and she still grieved for him. To live or to die was of no consequence to her.

She performed her work as usual about the quiet camp. Even when the sun set and there was nothing for her to do, the widow carried her tanning frame into her tepee to work by the light of her fire and the birchbark cone she had thrust into her beaded headband, like a torch.

As she scraped the hide, the widow became aware of strangers just outside her lodge. A moment later the door flap was raised and six Sioux warriors entered. They carried bow and arrows and tomahawks in their belts. She knew she must die.

"Sit down and eat before you slay me," she said quietly.

Without a word the men sat down, three on each side of the entrance. The widow's invitation was not strange. Many warriors facing death committed an act of supreme courage or service, and it was the custom to permit those doomed to die, a last request.

The woman with the torch on her head set fresh meat and berries on birch-bark platters. She passed these to the men seated on the ground. When their hands were full she darted from the tent and ran towards the river.

The torch on her head made it easy for the Sioux to follow her and the warriors were right behind, shouting and yelling their rage. When the widow came to the edge of the cut bank she tore the torch from her headband and threw it ahead, and then dropped to the ground crouching low.

The Sioux chasing the light plunged over the cut bank to their death on the rocks below.

The woman listened to their cries for a time to see if all had really fallen and she was safe. Now she was too frightened to spend the night in her own tepee so she began to run westward where she knew her band would be camped in readiness for the big buffalo hunt.

She ran all through the night and it was sunrise when she saw the familiar lodges in the distance. The guards had seen the lone figure and rode out to discover who it was. One was waving his blanket in a friendly signal. They were certainly surprised to see the widow.

The people of the camp listened in disbelief as she told her story. Could a lone woman outwit six cunning Sioux? Was she telling this wild story to win honour for herself?

The chief ordered a fast pony for the widow and he with twenty of his men rode back to the four tepees by the Assiniboine River. As the men peered over the edge of the cut bank and saw the six bodies they knew that the woman's story was true. They made their way down to the rocks below and six scalps were taken as proof of what had happened.

The widow rode back with the chief, his men following, all singing the Hero Song to let the women in camp know that they must prepare a feast in the widow's honour. That night all sat around the campfire and watched as she who was now called the Torch Woman danced and enacted the story of her experience.

The chief proclaimed the widow a heroine. "Had our enemies killed her they would have hidden in our lodges there and waited our return and killed us all. Truly this woman is one of the great hero-queens to be honoured for all time."

Torch Woman was greatly admired for all her life after that. She received many gifts and many offers of marriage.

GLOSSARY

band   group of people organized together. In 1990 there were 596 native bands in Canada, some economically poor and some quite prosperous.

Brandon   city in Manitoba

cone   a dry fruit of a tree with scales enclosing seeds

coyotes   small animals related to the American wolf
cut bank   rising ground at the edge of a river
Indians   Canada's native or indigenous peoples consist of

  1) Indians (there are more than 400,000 status Indians, recognized as Indi-
     an by the federal government, as well as non-status Indians, to equal more
     than one million of at least partial ancestry)
  2) Inuit (there are about 28,000 [1988]), and
  3) Métis (there were about 98,000 in the 1981 census, a low estimate).

They are represented in Canada by the Assembly of First Nations (status Indians) and the Native Council of Canada (non-status and Métis). Some native
people prefer to be called First Nations to indicate that they were originally separate nations.
scalps   an ancient way of counting the dead of the enemy in war.
Stone Roasters   note that native names often are descriptive
tepees   tents which some native peoples lived in long ago

(Information on native peoples is from McMillan (1988) and Comeau and Santin
(1990))

A CLOSER READING

1. What is the setting for this story? What can you tell from the first two paragraphs about the way of life of these people (housing, food, occupations)?

2. Why does the widow want to stay in the camp? Why doesn't she care if she
   dies? Is she sincere? How long has her husband been dead?

3. What is her occupation? What does she wear on her head? Why does she
   wear it?

4. What is the woman's invitation to the Sioux? Is it strange?

5. What is her plan? Does she succeed?

6. How do her people react to her story?

7. Why do her people make her a hero-queen? Why did she get many offers of
   marriage?

CULTURAL DISCUSSION

1. In this story we see what the widow does, but we do not know what is on her
   mind. For instance, we do not know when she gets the plan to trick the Sioux
   warriors or how she is feeling when she asks them to sit down and eat. What
   do you think the purpose of this story was when it was first told, long ago?

2. Were you surprised that the widow was allowed to stay in the camp alone? What does this tell you about this band? About women's roles and rights?

3. Some native women were allowed to become warriors if they so wished. What do think of this practice?

4. The widow received many offers of marriage. What do you suppose (guess) the widow looked for in a husband? (Use your imagination or do some research on native culture at the library.)

5. What do (did) you look for in a husband/wife? Is it similar to other people in the place where you grew up? Is it different from the Canadians you have observed? Do circumstances such as wars and hardship play a part in someone's choice of a marriage partner?

6. This very old story, which the father and son (Alex Grisdale) were anxious to preserve, must reveal what was traditionally important to the Brokenhead Reserve in Manitoba. Is there any point in telling such stories today? Why should you read the literature of sixty or more years ago? Is the literature of your first language being preserved?

7. What values of native peoples does this story convey? Do you know any other values? How could you find out?

LOOKING AT LANGUAGE

Understatement

When stories are retold, as this one was when it was written down, they are often simpler in form than the original. But even oral native literature includes *understatement* (saying things in a way that is restrained or held back) and an absence of strong personal emotion. Do you see these features in "The Torch Woman"? Is there any place in the story where you might expect to see strong emotion? Are these features a part of the literature of your first language? Is there another story you have read in this text which seems "understated" in style?

Allegory

An *allegory* is a story in which the characters represent ideals. Could this story be an allegory? What would the ideal be? Can you remember an allegory from your first culture? If so, what is the ideal which is represented? (Remember that we are not always conscious or aware of the myths and allegories that we grew up with because they are so much a part of us.)

REINFORCING SKILLS

Outline "The Torch Woman" using the format introduced after "A Secret Lost in the Water".

ACTIVITIES

Storytelling

Invent or translate from your first language a legend related to your culture. Share it with the class so that they will know more about what is important to you and your ancestors. Write an outline first to help you organize your story. Begin with important information about the setting.

Essay Writing

In a paragraph, describe what the woman does and why it is heroic. Use the present tense (often used by critics when discussing fiction) or the past tense. Be consistent.

References

Comeau, P. and Aldo Santin. *The First Canadians*. Toronto: James Lorimer & Company. 1990.

Grant, A. *Our Bit of Truth*. Winnipeg: Pemmican Publications, 1990.

McMillan, A.D. *Native Peoples and Cultures of Canada*. Vancouver: Douglas & McIntyre, 1988.

THE DEAD CHILD
GABRIELLE ROY
(1909-1983)

Translated by Joyce Marshall

Gabrielle Roy was born in Saint-Boniface, Manitoba, of French-Canadi-an parents. She taught for several years in Manitoba's rural schools much like the one described in "The Dead Child". Winner of many honours for her writing (in French), including two Governor General's Awards, Gabrielle Roy is a favourite author of many Canadians. Her novels include The Tin Flute *(1947) and* Where Nests the Water Hen *(1951). "The Dead Child" is from a collection of stories called* Enchanted Summer *(1976).*

PREPARING TO READ

This story, set in a small village in Manitoba in the late 1920s or 1930s, is about a teacher remembering her first job as a substitute teacher in the month of June. What do you think a rural school was like in Canada in those days? What problems might a substitute (non-permanent) teacher expect to have?

The children are very polite. Is this how children are supposed to be in school? What is the "ideal" student like? The "ideal" teacher? What do you think children are like in Canadian schools today?

The children in this story are Métis (the descendants of French-Canadian hunters and trappers and native people). Do you think they were very different from children in other parts of Canada?

Why then did the memory of that dead child seek me out in the very midst of the summer that sang?

When till then no intimation of sorrow had come to me through the dazzling revelations of that season.

I had just arrived in a very small village in Manitoba to finish the school year as replacement for a teacher who had fallen ill or simply, for all I know, become discouraged.

The principal of the Normal School had called me to his office towards the end of my year's study. "Well," he said, "there's a school available for the month of June. It's not much but it's an opportunity. When the time comes for you to apply for a permanent position, you'll be able to say you've had experience. Believe me, it's a help."

And so I found myself at the beginning of June in that very poor village—just a few shacks built on sand, with nothing around it but spindly spruce trees. "A month," I asked myself, "will that be long enough for me to become attached to the children or for the children to become attached to me? Will a month be worth the effort?"

Perhaps the same calculation was in the minds of the children who presented themselves at school that first day of June—"Is this teacher going to stay long enough to be worth the effort?"—for I had never seen children's faces so deject-ed, so apathetic, or perhaps sorrowful. I had had so little experience. I myself was hardly more than a child.

Nine o'clock came. The room was hot as an oven. Sometimes in Manitoba, espe-cially in the sandy areas, an incredible heat settles in during the first days of June.

Scarcely knowing where or how to begin, I opened the attendance book and called the roll. The names were for the most part very French and today they still return to my memory, like this, for no reason: Madeleine Bérubé, Josephat Bris-set, Emilien Dumont, Cécile Lépine....

But most of the children who rose and answered "Present, mamzelle," when their names were called had the slightly narrowed eyes, warm colouring and jet black hair that told of métis blood.

They were beautiful and exquisitely polite; there was really nothing to reproach them for except the inconceivable distance they maintained between themselves and me. It crushed me. "Is this what children are like then," I asked myself with anguish, "untouchable, barricaded in some region where you can't reach them?"

I came to the name Yolande Chartrand.

No one answered. It was becoming hotter by the minute. I wiped a bit of per-spiration from my forehead. I repeated the name and, when there was still no answer, I looked up at faces that seemed to me completely indifferent.

Then from the back of the classroom, above the buzzing of flies, there arose a voice I at first couldn't place. "She's dead, mamzelle. She died last night."

Perhaps even more distressing than the news was the calm level tone of the child's voice. As I must have seemed unconvinced, all the children nodded gravely as if to say, "It's true."

Suddenly a sense of impotence greater than any I can remember weighed upon me.

"Ah," I said, lost for words.

"She's already laid out," said a boy with eyes like coals. "They're going to bury her for good tomorrow."

"Ah," I repeated.

The children seemed a little more relaxed now and willing to talk, in snatches and at long intervals.

A boy in the middle of the room offered, "She got worse the last two months."

We looked at one another in silence for a long time, the children and I. I now understood that the expression in their eyes that I had taken for indifference was a heavy sadness. Much like this stupefying heat. And we were only at the beginning of the day.

"Since Yolande... has been laid out," I suggested, "and she was your schoolmate... and would have been my pupil... would you like... after school at four o'clock... for us to go and visit her?"

On the small, much too serious faces there appeared the trace of a smile, wary, still very sad but a sort of smile just the same.

"It's agreed then, we'll go to visit her, her whole class."

From that moment, despite the enervating heat and the sense that haunted us all, I feel sure that human efforts are all ultimately destined to a sort of failure, the children fixed their attention as much as possible on what I was teaching and I did my best to rouse their interest.

At five past four I found most of them waiting for me at the door, a good twenty children but making no more noise than if they were being kept in after school. Several of them went ahead to show me the way. Others pressed around me so closely I could scarcely move. Five or six of the smaller ones took me by the hand or the shoulder and pulled me forward gently as if they were leading a blind person. They did not talk, merely held me enclosed in their circle.

Together, in this way, we followed a track through the sand. Here and there thin spruce trees formed little clumps. The air was now barely moving. In no time the village was behind us—forgotten, as it were.

We came to a wooden cabin standing in isolation among the little trees. Its door was wide open, so we were able to see the dead child from quite far off. She had been laid out on rough boards suspended between two straight chairs set back to back. There was nothing else in the room. Its usual contents must have been crowded into the only other room of the house for, besides a stove and table and a few pots on the floor, I could see a bed and a mattress piled with clothes. But no chairs. Clearly the two used as supports for the boards on which the dead child lay were the only ones in the house.

The parents had undoubtedly done all they could for their child. They had covered her with a clean sheet. They had given her a room to herself. Her mother, probably, had arranged her hair in the two very tight braids that framed the thin face. But some pressing need had sent them away: perhaps the purchase of a coffin in town or a few more boards to make her one themselves. At any rate, the dead child was alone in the room that had been emptied for her—alone, that is to say, with the flies. A faint odour of death must have attracted them. I saw one with a blue body walk over her forehead. I immediately placed myself near her head and began to move my hand back and forth to drive the flies away.

The child had a delicate little face, very wasted, with the serious expression I had seen on the faces of most of the children here, as if the cares of the adults had crushed them all too early. She might have been ten or eleven years old. If she had lived a little longer, I reminded myself, she would have been one of my pupils. She would have learned something from me. I would have given her something to keep. A bond would have been formed between me and this little stranger—who knows, perhaps even for life.

As I contemplated the dead child, those words "for life"—as if they implied a long existence—seemed to me the most rash and foolish of all the expressions we use so lightly.

In death the child looked as if she were regretting some poor little joy she had never known. I continued at least to prevent the flies from settling upon her. The children were watching me. I realized that they now expected everything from me, though I didn't know much more than they and was just as confused. Still I had a sort of inspiration.

"Don't you think Yolande would like to have someone with her always till the time comes to commit her to the ground?"

The faces of the children told me I had struck the right note.

"We'll take turns then, four or five around her every two hours, until the funeral."

They agreed with a glow in their dark eyes.

"We must be careful not to let the flies touch Yolande's face."

They nodded to show they were in agreement. Standing around me, they now felt a trust in me so complete it terrified me.

In a clearing among the spruce trees a short distance away, I noticed a bright pink stain on the ground whose source I didn't yet know. The sun slanted upon it, making it flame, the one moment in this day that had been touched by a certain grace.

"What sort of girl was she?" I asked.

At first the children didn't understand. Then a boy of about the same age said with tender seriousness, "She was smart, Yolande."

The other children looked as if they agreed.

"And did she do well in school?"

"She didn't come very often this year. She was always being absent."

"Our teacher before last this year said Yolande could have done well."

"How many teachers have you had this year?"

"You're the third, mamzelle. I guess the teachers find it too lonesome here."

"What did Yolande die of?"

"T.B., mamzelle," they replied with a single voice, as if this was the customary way for children to die around here.

They were eager to talk about her now. I had succeeded in opening the poor little doors deep within them that no one perhaps had ever much wanted to see opened. They told me moving facts about her brief life. One day on her way home from school—it was in February; no, said another, in March—she had lost her reader and wept inconsolably for weeks. To study her lesson after that, she had to borrow a book from one of the others—and I saw on the faces of some of them that they'd grudged lending their readers and would always regret this. Not having a dress for her first communion, she entreated till her mother finally made her one from the only curtain in the house: "the one from this room...a beautiful lace curtain, mamzelle."

"And did Yolande look pretty in her lace curtain dress?" I asked.

They all nodded deeply, in their eyes the memory of a pleasant image.

I studied the silent little face. A child who had loved books, solemnity and decorous attire. Then I glanced again at the astonishing splash of pink in the melancholy landscape. I realized suddenly that it was a mass of wild roses. In June they open in great sheets all over Manitoba, growing from the poorest soil. I felt some alleviation.

"Let's go and pick some roses for Yolande."

On the children's faces there appeared the same slow smile of gentle sadness I had seen when I suggested visiting the body.

In no time we were gathering roses. The children were not yet cheerful, far from that, but I could hear them at least talking to one another. A sort of rivalry had gripped them. Each vied to see who could pick the most roses or the brightest, those of a deep shade that was almost red.

From time to time one tugged at my sleeve, "Mamzelle, see the lovely one I've found!"

On our return we pulled them gently apart and scattered petals over the dead child. Soon only her face emerged from the pink drift. Then—how could this be?— it looked a little less forlorn.

The children formed a ring around their schoolmate and said of her without the bitter sadness of the morning, "She must have got to heaven by this time."

Or, "She must be happy now."

I listened to them, already consoling themselves as best they could for being alive.

But why, oh why, did the memory of that dead child seek me out today in the very midst of the summer that sang?

Was it brought to me just now by the wind with the scent of roses?

A scent I have not much liked since the long ago June when I went to that poorest of villages—to acquire, as they say, experience.

GLOSSARY

alleviation   lessening of pain

apathetic   unenthusiastic

barricaded   (*poetic*) protected by a wall

bond   connection

braids   arrangement for hair

calculation   here it means "question"

coffin   box to bury the dead

commit   put

dazzling revelations   very exciting discoveries

decorous attire   attractive clothes

dejected   sad

first communion   Catholic religion ritual when children first receive the bread that they believe is Jesus Christ's body

funeral   ceremony when the dead are being buried

impotence   powerlessness

intimation   hint

isolation   alone

laid out   (a dead person) dressed in a special gown or suit, viewed by loved ones who come to say goodbye

mamzelle   Miss (short form of French word Mademoiselle)

melancholy   sad

midst   middle

Normal School   a school for teachers-in-training

rash   done too fast

ritual   a ceremony, part of a culture which is repeated

roll   list of names

scarcely   hardly

sheets   (*poetic*) description of how the many flowers together look

solemnity   seriousness

struck the right note   said the right thing

summer that sang   (*poetic*) a very happy time

T.B.   tuberculosis, a disease of the lungs that was common in Canada until recent times

trace   hint
wasted   thin, after an illness

A CLOSER READING

1. The first sentence tells us that this story is about a sad memory of a summer long ago. The person telling the story had just arrived in a small village in Manitoba. Why was she there?

2. What is the village like? What is the teacher worried about?

3. What do the children's faces show? Why does the teacher think they are dejected (depressed)? Is she correct?

4. What is the weather like? What feeling do we have as the story begins—is it a happy feeling? Why or why not?

5. The names of the children are all French. Is that surprising in Manitoba? How are the faces of the children described?

6. Describe the young teacher. How is she feeling when she goes to the school?

7. What has happened to make the children feel the way they do? What does the teacher suggest they do? Is it a good idea?

8. What is the cabin like? Are the parents rich or poor? How do you know? How do the children describe Yolande?

9. What does the child mean when he says that the last teacher might have been lonely?

10. Why does the teacher suggest they take turns driving away the flies? Why does picking roses brighten their faces?

11. Why might the character telling the story remember this sad experience years later when she is having a wonderful summer? Does she like the smell of roses now? Why or why not?

CULTURAL DISCUSSION

1. This story is set in a rural school many years ago. What was your school like and who was your favourite teacher?

2. A ritual is described for handling the terrible feelings of loss over the death of a friend. What is the ritual as described in this story? Does it make the mourners feel better? Why? Do you understand this ritual? Is this similar to or different from the death ritual where you grew up?

3. The people in this rural community know each other well. Do you think the previous teachers have belonged to this community? Is this your idea of a

Canadian community? Explain. Have you experienced this kind of community elsewhere? What kind of community life do you prefer?

4. Why is this teacher able to communicate with the Métis children? What does
    "communicate" mean?

5. What do you imagine a wedding would be like in this village? What is a wed-
    ding like in your home town?

LOOKING AT LANGUAGE

Imagery and Figures of Speech

"The Dead Child" begins with a sentence about a memory seeking out the narrator, during a summer that sang. Can a memory seek someone? Can summer sing?
In poetry, such things happen. This fiction, like Buckler's, is quite poetic, full of
imagery: vivid, lively descriptions which appeal to our senses.

Sometimes imagery (mental pictures) says one thing and means another, for
example, Robert Burn's poem title, "My Love is Like a Red, Red Rose". A comparison
using "like" or "as" is called a *simile*. A *metaphor* omits the "like" or "as" but still makes
a comparison, for example, "my sweet love", comparing a person to something that
tastes sweet. Similes and metaphors are called *figures of speech*.

"*A summer that sang*" means a summer that was joyful (like a person who sings).
The sad memory came in a summer of happy times, but the narrator asks why
because it is not strictly logical and is perhaps ironic (the opposite of what we expect).

We also use similes and metaphors in everyday language when we describe
things as if they were people, and people as if they were things:

- The arms of a chair.
- That person seemed as cold as ice (or very warm).
- She was as busy as a bee.
- He's the apple of my eye.
- She's a peach.
- I feel so blue.

1. Finish these sentences with figurative language (use translation of words from
    your first language, if you like).

    a. I am as happy as a...
    b. She sings like a...
    c. He is as tall as a...
    d. She's as funny as a...

Popular songs use metaphorical language. Have you heard the song "Blue
Moon"? What emotions do colours signify? How are these different in other
languages and cultures?

2. Sometimes we join nouns to unusual adjectives to make a description come alive. Match the following nouns with unusual adjectives, such as dancing, coughing, sour, hurt. Explain your choices.

    a. A musical note that was...
    b. An automobile that was...
    c. The young girl's eyes were...
    d. A memory that...

3. Search through "The Dead Child" for four examples of similes and metaphors.

4. Describe someone you know, or some place you have been, using similes.

REINFORCING SKILLS

1. Look at "A Penny in the Dust" again and find four examples of figurative language. Explain how they work.

2. Look at "The Torch Woman" again. What do you think the word "torch" might represent (figuratively) to native people?

ACTIVITIES

Essay Writing

1. In a paragraph or a short essay, describe the village with the school and Yolande's house *or* describe the room where Yolande is laid out. Give details from the text.

2. In a paragraph or a short essay, describe what the teacher asks the children to do at Yolande's house and explain why they seem to like it.

LIES MY FATHER TOLD ME
TED ALLAN
(b. 1916)

Ted Allan was born in Montreal and is the author of the award-winning screenplays, Lies My Father Told Me *and* Love Streams; *co-author of* The Scalpel, The Sword, The Story of Dr. Norman Bethune; *and author of* Love is a Long Shot *and of the internationally published children's book,* Willie, the Squowse, *now translated into ten languages. His short stories have appeared in* The New Yorker, Harper's *and other journals.*

PREPARING TO READ

In "Lies My Father Told Me", set in the 1920s, the narrator remembers the good times he had with his grandfather when he was growing up in a Jewish neighbourhood in Montreal. What do you think life was like in the 1920s? In Montreal? In your hometown?

Have your grandparents played an important part in your life? Do you know stories about them, or stories told by them? Will you pass them on to your grandchildren? Share a story with the class.

My grandfather stood six feet three in his worn-out bedroom slippers. He had a long grey beard with streaks of white running through it. When he prayed, his voice boomed like a choir as he turned the pages of his prayerbook with one hand and stroked his beard with the other. His hands were bony and looked like tree-roots; they were powerful. My grandpa had been a farmer in the old country. In Montreal he conducted what he called 'a second-hand business'.

In his youth, I was told, Grandpa had been something of a wild man, drinking and playing with the village wenches until my grandmother took him in hand. In his old age, when I knew him, he had become a very religious man. He prayed three times a day on week-days and all day on Saturday. In between prayers he rode around on a wagon which, as I look back, rolled on despite all the laws of physics and mechanics. Its four wheels always seemed to be going in every direction but forwards. The horse that pulled the wagon was called Ferdeleh. He was my pet and it was only much later, when I had seen many other horses, that I realized that Ferdeleh was not everything a horse could have been. His belly hung very low, almost touching the street when he walked. His head went back and forth in jerky motions in complete disharmony with the rest of him. He moved slowly, almost painfully, apparently realizing that he was capable of only one speed and determined to go no faster or slower than the rate he had established some time back. Next to Grandpa I loved Ferdeleh best, with the possible exception of God, or my mother when she gave me candy.

On Sundays, when it didn't rain, Grandpa, Ferdeleh, and myself would go riding through the back lanes of Montreal. The lanes then were not paved as they are now, and after a rainy Saturday, the mud would be inches deep and the wagon heaved and shook like a barge in a stormy sea. Ferdeleh's pace remained, as always, the same. He liked the mud. It was easy on his feet.

When the sun shone through my windows on Sunday morning I would jump out of bed, wash, dress, run into the kitchen where Grandpa and I said our morning prayers, and then we'd both go to harness and feed Ferdeleh. On Sundays Ferdeleh would whinny like a happy child. He knew it was an extra special day for all of us. By the time he had finished his oats and hay Grandpa and I would be finished with our breakfast which Grandma and Mother had prepared for us.

Then we'd go through what Grandpa called 'the women's Sunday song'. It went like this: 'Don't let him hold the reins crossing streets. Be sure to come back if it starts to rain. Be sure not to let him hold the reins crossing streets. Be sure to come back if it starts to rain.' They would repeat this about three hundred times until Grandpa and I were weary from nodding our heads and saying, 'Yes'. We could hear it until we turned the corner and went up the lane of the next street.

Then began the most wonderful of days as we drove through the dirt lanes of Montreal, skirting the garbage cans, jolting and bouncing through the mud and dust, calling every cat by name and every cat meowing its hello, and Grandpa and I holding our hands to our ears and shouting out at the top of our lungs, 'Regs, cloze, botels! Regs, cloze, botels!'

What a wonderful game that was! I would run up the back stairs and return with all kinds of fascinating things, old dresses, suits, pants, rags, newspapers, all shapes of bottles, all shapes of trash, everything you can think of, until the wagon was filled.

Sometimes a woman would ask me to send Grandpa up to give her a price on what she had, and Grandpa would shout up from downstairs, 'My feet ache. The boy will give you a price.' I knew what he offered for an old suit, for an old dress, and I would shout down describing the items in question and the state of deterioration. For clothes that were nothing better than rags we offered a standard price, 'Fifteen cents, take it or leave it.' Clothes that might be repaired I would hold out for Grandpa to see and he'd appraise them. And so we'd go through the lanes of the city.

Sometimes the women would not be satisfied with the money Grandpa had given me for them. Grandpa would always say, 'Eleshka, women always want more than they get. Remember that. Give them a finger and they want the whole hand.'

My Sunday rides were the happiest times I spent. Sometimes Grandpa would let me wear his derby hat which came down over my ears, and people would look at me and laugh and I'd feel even happier feeling how happy everyone was on Sunday.

Sometimes strange, wonderful smells would come over the city, muffling the smell of the garbage cans. When this happened we would stop Ferdeleh and breathe deeply. It smelled of sea and of oak trees and flowers. Then we knew we were near the mountain in the centre of the city and that the wind from the river was bringing the perfumes of the mountain and spraying it over the city. Often we would ride out of the back lanes and up the mountain road. We couldn't go too far up because it was a strain on Ferdeleh. As far as we went, surrounded on each side by tall poplars and evergreens, Grandpa would tell me about the old country, about the rivers and the farms, and sometimes he'd get off the wagon and pick up some black earth in his hands. He'd squat, letting the earth fall between his fingers, and I'd squat beside him doing the same thing.

When we came to the mountain Grandpa's mood would change and he would talk to me of the great land that Canada was, and of the great things the young people growing up were going to do in this great land. Ferdeleh would walk to the edge of the road and eat the thick grass on the sides. Grandpa was at home among the trees and black earth and thick grass and on our way down the mountain road he would sing songs that weren't prayers, but happy songs in Russian. Sometimes he'd clap his hands to the song as I held the reins and Ferdeleh would look back at him and shake his head with pleasure. One Sunday on our ride home through the mountain a group of young boys and girls threw stones at us and shouted in French: *'Juif... Juif... !'* Grandpa held his strong arm around me, cursed back muttering 'anti-Semites' under his breath. When I asked him what he said he answered, 'It is something I hope you never learn.' The boys and girls laughed and got tired of throwing stones. That was the last Sunday we went to the mountain.

If it rained on Sunday my mother wouldn't let me go out, so every Saturday evening I prayed for the sun to shine on Sunday. Once I almost lost faith in God and in the power of prayer but Grandpa fixed it. For three Sundays in succession it rained. In my desperation I took it out on God. What was the use of praying to Him if He didn't listen to you? I complained to Grandpa.

'Perhaps you don't pray right,' he suggested.

'But I do. I say, Our God in heaven, hallowed be Thy name, Thy will on earth as it is in heaven. Please don't let it rain tomorrow.'

'Ah! In English you pray?' my grandfather exclaimed triumphantly.

'Yes,' I answered.

'But God only answers prayers in Hebrew. I will teach you how to say that prayer in Hebrew. And, if God doesn't answer, it's your own fault. He's angry because you didn't use the Holy Language.' But God wasn't angry because next Sunday the sun shone its brightest and the three of us went for our Sunday ride.

On weekdays, Grandpa and I rose early, a little after daybreak, and said our morning prayers. I would mimic his sing-song lamentations, sounding as if my heart were breaking and wondering why we both had to sound so sad. I must have put everything I had into it because Grandpa assured me that one day I would become a great cantor and a leader of the Hebrews. 'You will sing so that the ocean will open up a path before you and you will lead our people to a new paradise.'

I was six then and he was the only man I ever understood even when I didn't understand his words. I learned a lot from him. If he didn't learn a lot from me, he made me feel he did.

I remember once saying, 'You know, sometimes I think I'm the son of God. Is it possible?'

'It is possible,' he answered, 'but don't rely on it. Many of us are sons of God. The important thing is not to rely too much upon it. The harder we work, the harder we study, the more we accomplish, the surer we are that we are sons of God.'

At the synagogue on Saturday his old, white-bearded friends would surround me and ask me questions. Grandpa would stand by and burst with pride. I strutted like a peacock.

'Who is David?' the old men would ask me.

'He's the man with the beard, the man with the bearded words.' And they laughed.

'And who is God?' they would ask me.

'King and Creator of the Universe, the All-Powerful One, the Almighty One, more powerful even than Grandpa.' They laughed again and I thought I was pretty smart. So did Grandpa. So did my grandmother and my mother.

So did everyone, except my father. I didn't like my father. He said things to me like, 'For God's sake, you're smart, but not as smart as you think. Nobody is that smart.' He was jealous of me and he told me lies. He told me lies about Ferdeleh.

'Ferdeleh is one part horse, one part camel, and one part chicken,' he told me. Grandpa told me that was a lie, Ferdeleh was all horse. 'If he is part anything, he is part human,' said Grandpa. I agreed with him. Ferdeleh understood everything we said to him. No matter what part of the city he was in, he could find his way home, even in the dark.

'Ferdeleh is going to collapse one day in one heap,' my father said. 'Ferdeleh is carrying twins.' 'Ferdeleh is going to keel over one day and die.' 'He should be shot now or he'll collapse under you one of these days,' my father would say. Neither I nor Grandpa had much use for the opinions of my father.

On top of everything, my father had no beard, didn't pray, didn't go to the synagogue on the Sabbath, read English books and never read the prayer books, played piano on the Sabbath and sometimes would draw my mother into his villainies by making her sing while he played. On the Sabbath this was an abomination to both Grandpa and me.

One day I told my father, 'Papa, you have forsaken your forefathers.' He burst out laughing and kissed me and then my mother kissed me, which infuriated me all the more.

I could forgive my father these indignities, his not treating me as an equal, but I couldn't forgive his telling lies about Ferdeleh. Once he said that Ferdeleh 'smelled up' the whole house, and demanded that Grandpa move the stable. It was true that the kitchen, being next to the stable, which was in the back shed, did sometimes smell of hay and manure but, as Grandpa said, 'What is wrong with such a smell? It is a good healthy smell.'

It was a house divided, with my grandmother, mother, and father on one side, and Grandpa, Ferdeleh, and me on the other.

One day a man came to the house and said he was from the Board of Health and that the neighbours has complained about the stable. Grandpa and I knew we were beaten then. You could get around the Board of Health, Grandpa informed me, if you could grease the palms of the officials. I suggested the obvious but Grandpa explained that this type of 'grease' was made of gold. The stable would have to be moved. But where?

As it turned out, Grandpa didn't have to worry about it. The whole matter was taken out of his hands a few weeks later.

Next Sunday the sun shone brightly and I ran to the kitchen to say my prayers with Grandpa. But Grandpa wasn't there. I found my grandmother there instead—weeping. Grandpa was in his room ill. He had a sickness they call diabetes and at that time the only thing you could do about diabetes was weep. I fed Ferdeleh and soothed him because I knew how disappointed he was.

That week I was taken to an aunt of mine. There was no explanation given. My parents thought I was too young to need any explanations. On Saturday next I was brought home, too late to see Grandpa that evening, but I felt good knowing that I would spend the next day with him and Ferdeleh again.

When I came to the kitchen Sunday morning Grandpa was not there. Ferdeleh was not in the stable. I thought they were playing a joke on me so I rushed to the front of the house expecting to see Grandpa sitting atop the wagon waiting for me.

But there wasn't any wagon. My father came up behind me and put his hand on my head. I looked up questioningly and he said, 'Grandpa and Ferdeleh have gone to heaven....'

When he told me they were never coming back, I moved away from him and went to my room. I lay down on my bed and cried, not for Grandpa and Ferdeleh, because I knew they would never do such a thing to me, but about my father, because he had told me such a horrible lie.

GLOSSARY

abomination something shocking or disgusting

anti-Semite prejudiced against Jews

appraise estimate the worth of something

cantor the person who leads the community in song in a Hebrew synagogue (place of worship)

David Old Testament figure of a brave young man who slays an evil giant, Goliath

grease the palms pay someone to do something (bribery)

Juif... the word Jew in French, meant to be insulting

ocean will open up a path recalls in the Old Testament when Moses led the Israelites out of Egypt and slavery in ancient times

'Regs, cloze, botels!' 'rags, clothes, bottles', called out with a Yiddish accent (a dialect of Hebrew)

Saturday the Sabbath, the holy day in the Hebrew religion

second-hand business sells items that are not new

six feet three about 190 centimetres

wenches obsolete term for young women who drink with men

A CLOSER READING

1. Describe the grandfather. Can you draw a picture of him from the details in the story? What was his occupation before he came to Canada? Where do you think he lived before? Was he happy in Canada? What did he do for a living in Canada? What was he like as a young man? Did he change as he got older?

2. The boy loves the horse, Ferdeleh. What's the horse like? Why do you think the boy loves him?

3. Describe in detail the routine on a typical Sunday. Why is it so special? What is the "women's song"?

4. What is the relationship between the grandfather and the boy? Give details.

5. How does the grandfather's mood change when he comes to the mountain and feels the black earth?

6. Why do the children throw stones and shout insults at the boy and the old man? What does Grandpa mean when he says *"It is something I hope you never learn"*?

7. What is the little boy's idea of prayer? Is it the same as an adult's view of prayer?

8. Does the grandfather mean it when he says *"God only answers prayers in Hebrew"*? Why does he say it? Does the boy believe it?

9. What does the narrator mean when he says *"he was the only man I ever understood even when I didn't understand his words"*?

10. How does the grandfather show his love for the young boy?

11. How is his father's attitude different toward the boy? Why does he say he does not like his father? What "lies" does the father tell about the horse? Was the father really jealous of the boy? How does the text reveal that the father is different from the grandfather in his practice of religion?

12. Explain the family's problem with having the horse.

13. Explain the father's "horrible lie".

14. Is there humour in this story? Is the narrator laughing at the boy?

CULTURAL DISCUSSION

1. Does the grandfather remind you of anyone in your past? What are some of the roles a grandfather can play in the life of a small boy?

2. Does it surprise you to hear about pets being loved so much? How are pets regarded in the place where you grew up?

3. Did you grow up with a special day, for example, Friday or Sunday? What was the routine on that day?

4. Does the relationship between the grandfather and the boy seem typical of Canadians you observe? What are Canadian families like? Do you think they are different from or the same as families in other places? Explain. Why do you suppose the boy's view of his father is less sympathetic than of his grandfather? How does the role of a father usually differ from that of a grandfather?

5. What effect does scenery have on people? Are you happier when you are in the mountains, at the seashore, in the desert? The city or the country? Did coming to Canada mean a great change for you?

6. What does the black earth mean to the grandfather? What does this tell us about his values?

7. How do you explain the boys and girls who throw stones? Have you experienced or observed racial attacks on any group in Canada? Is this acceptable or is it condemned?

8. The grandfather and the boy do not return to the mountain after the racial attack. Why not? Can you protect children from racism?

9. Do all Canadians do similar things on Saturdays and Sundays? Fridays? Do most Canadians you know pray? Are Canadians, in general, public or private about prayer and religion?

10. Why doesn't Grandpa "grease the palms" of the officials? Does this usually work in Canada? Do Canadians have indirect ways of getting things done? Do most countries? Do you have any advice for newcomers to Canada? For newcomers to your country?

11. What do you tell children about death? Why do some Canadians have trouble talking about death? Is this common to all cultures? Does everyone cry or show emotion when someone close to them dies? Does showing emotion depend on culture?

12. Is the family in this story a happy one? Explain. How do you define a happy family?

LOOKING AT LANGUAGE

Defining Words from Context

When words in a story are unfamiliar, it is often possible to guess at their meaning by looking at the rest of the sentence, or by reading ahead. For example:

a. ...*streaks* **of white running through it**   "it" refers to the beard; white might refer to grey hair; streaks must be grey hairs in long, narrow lines. *Streaks are long, narrow lines.*

b. **...he had become a very** *religious* **man. He prayed...**   you do not know what "religious" means, but you may know what "prayed" means; you guess that religious has something to do with praying.

Guess the meaning of the following words and phrases from the story. Explain your guess.

1. choir
2. stroked
3. took him in hand
4. jerky
5. disharmony
6. heaved
7. barge
8. harness
9. skirting
10. deterioration

REINFORCING SKILLS

Paraphrase the first paragraph of the story. Does your paraphrase give the main idea? Paraphrase the second paragraph and ask someone else (a student or the instructor) if they understand the main idea.

ACTIVITIES

Storytelling

In many cultures oral storytelling is an important art and a means of handing down culture from one generation to the next. Does "Lies My Father Told Me" seem like a story that should be read aloud?

1. Read "Lies" out loud with feeling, as if you were telling the story to a friend.
2. Tell your own story to the class about someone who was important to you in your youth. You might begin the same way that Allan does, with a description of a person, and then continue with details of an event. Ask the class if they can tell why this story is important to you.

"Rules" for storytelling

a. Begin at the "point of innocence": tell your audience the background information they need to have in order to understand your story; for example, the time, the place, and any special information about the person in the story.

b. Keep your story short and lively so your listeners remain alert.

c. Practice your story and use a lively tone of voice. If you don't sound interesting, how can your audience be interested?

d. Enjoy yourself. Enjoyment is "catchy".

Essay Writing

Write a paragraph describing the grandfather or the child. Include evidence from the text to support your description.

PART II

ADAPTATIONS

The stories in **Part I: Legacies** look back, with some regret, on times in the past. The writers in **Part II: Adaptations** show a modern world in an urban setting where life is quite complicated. The mood is not nostalgic. The 1960s witnessed a cultural revolution in North America, and both "old" and "new" Canadians have had to adapt to many changes.

Relatively few people immigrated to Canada during the depression (1930-39) and World War II (1939-1945). After the war, however, people began to come again in great numbers, first from war-torn countries in Europe, and later from Asia, Africa and Latin America. The new immigrants brought their values to a rapidly changing culture. The government policy of multiculturalism (1971) encouraged immigrants to participate in all aspects of Canadian life, to learn one of Canada's official languages, but not to abandon the customs and values they brought to Canada. This kind of adjustment has not always been easy, and the stories by Himani Bannerji and Taien Ng show some of the issues that can cause difficulty.

Adaptation means adjustment to environmental conditions. The characters in these stories adapt to different kinds of changes in varying ways. See if you agree with their choices.

THE OTHER FAMILY
HIMANI BANNERJI
(b. 1942)

Himani Bannerji was born in Bangladesh when it was part of India. She received her M.A. in English and taught English in India. She emigrated to Canada in 1969 and is now a sociologist at York University in Toronto in addition to being a writer of fiction and poetry. Her works include a children's book, The Two Sisters *(1978), and a book of poetry,* Doing Time *(1986).*

PREPARING TO READ

Himani Bannerji's story, set in the 1970s or 1980s, is about a mother and child who have emigrated from a country like India or Bangladesh. What do you think might cause difficulty for such a family? How might their lives be complicated?

What about the word "family"? What does it mean to you? What does it mean to Canadians? Does it suggest different things to different people?

What does the word "identity" mean? Is it a problem for most people in Canada? Elsewhere?

If you have difficulty with the first paragraph, review the strategies after "Penny in the Dust".

When the little girl came home it was already getting dark. The winter twilight had transformed the sheer blue sky of the day into the colour of steel, on which were etched a few stars, the bare winter trees and the dark wedges of the house tops. A few lit windows cast a faint glow on the snow outside. The mother stood at her window and watched the little hooded figure walking toward the house. The child looked like a shadow, her blue coat blended into the shadows of the evening. This child, her own, how small and insubstantial she seemed, and how alone, walking home through a pavement covered with ice and snow! It felt unreal. So different was this childhood from her own, so far away from the sun, the trees and the peopled streets of her own country! What did I do, she thought, I took her away from her own people and her own language, and now here she comes walking alone, through an alien street in a country named Canada.

As she contemplated the solitary, moving figure, her own solitude rushed over her like a tide. She had drifted away from a world that she had lived in and understood, and now she stood here at the same distance from her home as from the homes which she glimpsed while walking past the sparkling clean windows of the sandblasted houses. And now the door bell rang, and here was her daughter scraping the snow off her boots on the door mat.

Dinner time was a good time. A time of warmth, of putting hot, steaming food onto the table. A time to chat about the important things of the day, a time to show each other what they had acquired. Sometimes, however, her mother would be absent-minded, worried perhaps about work, unsettled perhaps by letters that had arrived from home, scraping her feelings into a state of rawness. This was such an evening. She had served herself and her child, started a conversation about their two cats and fallen into a silence after a few minutes.

'You aren't listening to me, Mother.'

The complaining voice got through to her, and she looked at the indignant face demanding attention from the other side of the table. She gathered herself together.

'So what did he do, when you gave him dried food?'

'Oh, I don't quite remember, I think he scratched the ground near his bowl and left.'

The child laughed.

'That was smart of him! So why don't we buy tinned food for them?'

'Maybe we should,' she said, and tried to change the topic.

'So what did you do in your school today?'

'Oh, we drew pictures like we do every day. We never study anything—not like you said you did in school. We drew a family—our family. Want to see it?'

'Sure, and let's go to the living room, OK? This is messy.' Scraping of chairs and the lighting of the lamps in the other room. They both made a rush for the most comfortable chair, both reached it at the same time and made a compromise.

'How about you sit in my lap? No? OK, sit next to me then and we will squeeze in somehow.'

There was a remarkable resemblance between the two faces, except that the face of the child had a greater intensity, given by the wide open eyes. She was fine boned, and had black hair framing her face. Right now she was struggling with the contents of her satchel, apparently trying to feel her way to the paintings.

'Here it is,' she said, producing a piece of paper. 'Here's the family!'

The mother looked at the picture for a long time. She was very still. Her face had set into an expression of anger and sadness. She was trying very hard not to cry. She didn't want to frighten the child, and yet what she saw made her feel distant from her daughter, as though she was looking at her through the reverse end of a telescope. She couldn't speak at all. The little girl too sat very still, a little recoiled from the body of her mother, as though expecting a blow. Her hands were clenched into fists, but finally it was she who broke the silence.

'What's happened?' she said. 'Don't you like it?'

'Listen,' said the mother, 'this is not your family. I, you and your father are dark-skinned, dark-haired. I don't have a blond wig hidden in my closet, my eyes are black, not blue, and you father's beard is black, not red, and you, do you have a white skin, a button nose with freckles, blue eyes and blond hair tied into a pony tail? You said you drew our family. This is not it, is it?'

The child was now feeling distinctly cornered. At first she was startled and frightened by her mother's response, but now she was prepared to be defiant. She had the greatest authority behind her, and she now summoned it to her help.

'I drew it from a book,' she said, 'all our books have this same picture of the family. You can go and see it for yourself. And everyone else drew it too. You can ask our teacher tomorrow. She liked it, so there!'

The little girl was clutching at her last straw.

'But you? Where are you in this picture?' demanded her mother, by now thoroughly aroused. 'Where are we? Is this the family you would like to have? Don't you want us anymore? You want to be a *mem-sahib*, a white girl?'

But even as she lashed out these questions the mother regretted them. She could see that she made no sense to the child. She could feel the unfairness of it all. She was sorry that she was putting such a heavy burden on such young shoulders.

'First I bring her here,' she thought, 'and then I try to make her feel guilty for wanting to be the same as the others.' But something had taken hold of her this evening. Panic at the thought of losing her child, despair and guilt galvanized her into speech she regretted, and she looked with anger at her only child, who it seemed wanted to be white, who had rejected her dark mother. Someday this child would be ashamed of her, she thought, someday would move out into the world of those others. Someday they would be enemies. Confusing thoughts ran through her head like images on an uncontrollable television screen, in the chaos of which she heard her ultimate justification flung at her by her daughter—they wanted me to draw the family, didn't they? 'They' wanted 'her' to draw 'the family'. The way her daughter pronounced the words 'they' or 'the family' indicated that she knew what she was talking about. The simple pronoun 'they' definitely stood for authority, for that uncontrollable yet organized world immediately outside, of which the school was the ultimate expression. It surrounded their own private space. 'They' had power, 'they' could crush little people like her anytime 'they' wanted to, and in 'their' world that was the picture of the family. Whether her mother liked it or not, whether she looked like the little girl in it or not, made not one jot of difference. That was, yes, that was the right picture. As these thoughts passed through her mind, her anger ebbed away. Abandoning her fury and distance, the mother bowed her head at the image of this family and burst into sobs.

'What will happen to you?' she said. 'What did I do to you?'

She cried a great deal and said many incoherent things. The little girl was patient, quietly absorbing her mother's change of mood. She had a thoughtful look on her face, and bit her nails from time to time. She did not protest any more, but nor did she cry. After a while her mother took her to bed and tucked her in, and sat in the kitchen with the fearful vision of her daughter always outside of the window of the blond family, never the centre of her own life, always rejecting herself, and her life transformed into a gigantic peep show. She wept very bitterly because she had caused this destruction, and because she had hated her child in her own fear of rejection, and because she had sowed guilt into her mind.

When her mother went to bed and closed the door, the child, who had been waiting for long, left the bed. She crossed the corridor on her tiptoes, past the row of shoes, the silent gathering of the overcoats and the mirror with the wavy surface, and went into the washroom. Behind the door was another mirror, of full length, and clear. Deliberately and slowly the child took off the top of her pyjamas and surveyed herself with grave scrutiny. She saw the brownness of her skin, the wide, staring, dark eyes, the black hair now tousled from the pillows, the scar on her nose and the brownish pink of her mouth. She stood a while lost in this act of contemplation, until the sound of soft padded feet neared the door, and a whiskered face peeped in. She stooped and picked up the cat and walked back to her own room.

It was snowing again, and little elves with bright coloured coats and snow in their boots had reappeared in the classroom. When finally the coats were hung under pegs with names and boots neatly stowed away, the little girl approached her teacher. She had her painting from the day before in her hand.

'I have brought it back,' she said.

'Why?' asked her teacher, 'don't you like it any more?'

The little girl was looking around very intently.

'It's not finished yet,' she said. 'The books I looked at didn't have something. Can I finish it now?'

'Go ahead,' said the teacher, moving on to get the colours from the cupboard.

The little girl was looking at the classroom. It was full of children of all colours, of all kinds of shapes of noses and of different colours of hair. She sat on the floor, placed the incomplete picture on a big piece of newspaper and started to paint. She worked long at it—and with great concentration. Finally it was finished. She went back to her teacher.

'It's finished now,' she said, 'I drew the rest.'

The teacher reached out for the picture and spread it neatly on a desk. There they were, the blond family arranged in a semicircle with a dip in the middle, but next to them, arranged alike, stood another group—a man, a woman, and a child, but they were dark-skinned, dark-haired, the woman wore clothes from her own country, and the little girl in the middle had a scar on her nose.

'Do you like it?'

'Who are they?' asked the teacher, though she should have known. But the little girl didn't mind answering this question one bit.

'It's the other family,' she said.

GLOSSARY

all our books have this same picture   true at one time but now many school boards require books to reflect the backgrounds of the children

colour of steel   grey

clutching at her last straw   she could think of no more excuses

etched   cut

mem-sahib   *mem* is a variant of Ma'am and was used to address a white woman in India prior to Independence

peep show   before the age of television, a box containing moving pictures (usually indecent) seen through a small hole

recoiled   sprang back

reverse end of a telescope   makes objects appear far away

scar on her nose   traditional custom in India for a four- or five-year-old girl to have right side of her nose pierced to hang a piece of jewelry

so far away from the sun   Canada has winter for almost five months of the year, in contrast to India where it is warm all year

tinned food   more expensive than dried food

wedges   triangular shapes

A CLOSER READING

1. What is the main idea of the first paragraph? (Read past the words you don't understand.)
2. How does the mother feel about having brought her daughter to Canada?
3. In the second paragraph, when the mother says *"now she stood here at the same distance from her home as from the homes which she glimpsed..."*, what home is she talking about? Does she feel a part of the city surrounding her?
4. Why is the mother distracted today? Where do you think the father is?
5. Why does the mother try to change the topic when the child suggests they buy tinned food for the cats?
6. What does it mean when the little girl refuses to sit on her mother's lap?
7. What is the mother's reaction to the picture her daughter drew in school? Give details.
8. What is the daughter's reaction to her mother's behaviour?
9. Why do you think the little girl drew a picture of a white family? What does the narrator mean by *"putting such a heavy burden on her"*?
10. Paraphrase the mother's fears.
11. What is the little girl's motivation in the washroom?
12. How does the girl solve her problem? Do you think the mother will like it?
13. Is the character of the teacher realistic? Do you think a teacher would ask *"who are they"*?
14. Why doesn't the girl say *"It's my family"*?

CULTURAL DISCUSSION

1. Do you understand the mother's feeling in the first paragraph? Have you ever felt this way?
2. *"Dinner time was a good time."* Is this true in every country? Why or why not?
3. There are many kinds of foods for pets in Canada. Does this surprise you?
4. At what age do children wish to be independent in Canada? In other countries? What does independence mean?
5. Once you are in a new culture, should you want to be the same as the other members of the society? Should you try to keep your own identity?
6. Do young people in a family usually feel different from the older generations who come to a new country? Explain.
7. What do you imagine the mother would say when she saw "the other family"?

LOOKING AT LANGUAGE

Using Grammatical Clues

When two words are written together, or connected by *and*, you can often guess the meaning of one word if you know the meaning of the other, for example, *sparkling*, clean windows (clean windows give off flashes of light; they sparkle). Guess the meaning of the italicized words using the meaning of the other word for help.

1. *startled* and frightened
2. *absent-minded*, worried
3. *unsettled...*, scraping her feelings into... rawness
4. small and *insubstantial*
5. despair and *guilt*
6. hot, *steaming*

REINFORCING SKILLS

The first paragraph of "The Other Family" may include some words you are not familiar with, for example, *sheer*, *etched*, and *wedges*. Without these words, you can still get the main idea of the paragraph. But you should look at them more closely to see how the writer creates a mood and draws us in. Words like *dark* and *winter* are being used as *symbols* (words which stand for something else) to build an image of solitude and anxiety. What words indicate sadness or melancholy?

ACTIVITIES

Essay Writing

1. a. In a paragraph, explain how the mother feels at the beginning of the story and why she feels that way. Use the text for support.
   b. In an essay, explain how the mother feels at each stage of story. You might include how you think she will feel when she sees the revised painting.
2. In an essay, explain how you think the child feels
   a. at school when she completes the first painting,
   b. at home when her mother sees it, and
   c. at school when she revises it.

   Although this essay includes your own feelings, use the text for support.

SHUN-WAI
TAIEN NG
(b. 1970)

Taien Ng was born in 1970 in Vancouver. Her parents are from China. She is presently pursuing graduate studies in Montreal. Taien Ng has published other short stories as well as poems and plays. Her interests include theatre and cultural dilemmas; much of her work stems from her own experiences and ambitions.

PREPARING TO READ

Shun-Wai is Chinese for "Spirit Place", a special shrine where Chinese traditionally remember their ancestors. This custom, sometimes called ancestor worship, is no longer common in China, but the custom of having a shrine has been kept by some of the elderly in Hong Kong.

In this story the narrator watches her Canadian mother, who is a Christian, criticize her Hong Kong grandparents who have a Shun-Wai. Do religious practices usually change with each new generation? Can emigration cause this to happen? Does emigration widen the gulf between generations?

In the 1950s, some devout Catholics in North America had small altars in their homes to pray to Jesus and his mother, Mary. How does the ritual of praying vary among religions?

My mother's a strong woman, and she's also Christian. The two aren't synonymous, but they both describe her. I admire my mother a great deal, but this isn't something I'd readily admit. She'd only say, "You see? Mothers know best!" Then she'd move on to her speech about the inadequacies of my vegetarian diet.

When she came to Canada with my father some twenty-five years ago, she didn't have an inkling of the English language. Then my father left her. Now she's got an accounting business, and a house with a garden, and Jesus. And me, of course, which is probably why she turned to Jesus.

My mother and I aren't often on speaking terms any more. She says I'm like a gwua-mui—a white girl—never listen to the parents. I know I ought to be more patient with her, but we're both stubborn people. Anyway, I think it's good she has Jesus. Ever since I left home, she really has no one else.

Shun-Wai translates literally into "Spirit Place," a shrine for ancestral spirits. It can sometimes be quite large and take up a whole corner of a room with red lights, red and gold banners, and offerings. More often, though, it's very minimal like the one my grandparents, Poh Poh and Yeh Yeh, had. Theirs was tucked away in a space on the bookshelf and consisted of incense, a plate of oranges, and pictures of my great-grandparents.

When my mother saw the Shun-Wai, she tried to take it apart in the name of Christianity.

This is what I remember of Hong Kong: the stink of garbage and rotting food and sweat; narrow alleys crowded with beggars and people trying to sell their wares; chickens running loose; mosquitoes, flies, cockroaches. I went there with my mother for a week and a half, in the summer of my thirteenth birthday. It was Hong Kong, and not my mother, that made me realize I was Chinese.

We stayed with my grandparents, who lived in an apartment about the size of your average living-room. This included the kitchen, bathroom and bedroom—all squished into one living space. They were considered lucky to have so much room, since many families with twice the people lived in apartments half that size.

One night, all the relatives came over for dinner. In this small space were Poh Poh (Grandma) and Yeh Yeh (Grandpa), two uncles, one aunt, three cousins aged three to eight, my mother, and me. With everyone crowded around the table, Poh Poh began spooning out the soup.

My mother cleared her throat. "Put the soup down," she said to Poh Poh in Chinese. "We have to say grace."

Poh Poh hesitated, then put the soup down. My aunt, uncles and cousins looked bewildered. My mother held out her hand to me and told everyone to join hands. She closed her eyes.

"Thank you, Lord," she began, "for what we are about to receive, and thank you for this opportunity to have the family together."

I looked up. Poh Poh was staring at the soup. Yeh Yeh was looking at the rice. My aunt was looking at my uncle.

"Please, Lord," my mother continued, her eyes still tightly closed. "Please bless Poh Poh, Yeh Yeh, and my daughter, and..."

The electric fan whirred loudly. My five-year-old cousin kicked my three-year-old cousin under the table.

"Shhh!" my aunt hissed.

My eight-year-old cousin giggled.

"And forgive those who have turned their backs to you, Lord," my mother was saying. "Please help them find the way. Amen."

"Amen," I said when she opened her eyes and glared at me.

"Amen," murmured my aunt and my uncles, who were not sure what to say. Poh Poh picked up the pot of soup, and Yeh Yeh continued looking at the rice. My cousins kept giggling.

After dinner, Yeh Yeh left to see our relatives to the bus stop. It was then that my mother took notice of the Shun-Wai.

I also remember this about Hong Kong: it was so hot I could barely breathe. I sweated so much everything I touched felt sticky. Even after a shower, I would still feel grimy, as if there was a film over my skin. The big shopping centres were air-conditioned, but overly so, and when we went inside to escape the heat, I could always pass the time by counting the goosebumps on my skin.

There was nothing much to do but shop and visit relatives, which is not that exciting for a thirteen-year-old. All I wanted was a pizza, but every relative we saw took us out for Chinese food. I did not like Hong Kong.

Now that I'm older, I figure I'd been too young to fully appreciate the experience of another culture—which it was, after all. I understand Chinese well enough, but if you asked me to say anything in it, I'd probably stare at you dumbfounded. It's not that I don't know my own background. I know damn well I'm Chinese. My mother keeps reminding me of the fact. As if I would ever forget.

"What are you doing?" Poh Poh said as my mother bent to pick up the oranges. "Don't eat those, there are more oranges in the kitchen."

"How come you have a Shun-Wai?" my mother demanded.

"We've always had one... it's for your grandparents."

"You shouldn't have one," my mother said, raising her voice. "It's ancestral worship. These things aren't good. You shouldn't worship anything but God."

"Don't you want to remember your grandparents?"

"If you want to remember someone, then remember them here," my mother said loudly, tapping her head. "You don't need these sort of things."

"Tell your mother not to yell at me," Poh Poh said to me sadly.

"Mom," I said. "Stop yelling at your mother."

My mother ignored me and continued talking loudly for a while. Poh Poh just went into the kitchen. Yeh Yeh came back from the bus stop and then my mother talked at him, too. Finally they let her take the Shun-Wai apart, just to get some peace.

But what I really remember was the look on my grandparents' faces. I wanted to say something to them, but for the life of me, I didn't know how.

Sometimes on the weekends now, I like to take the bus into Chinatown and wander around. I'll go into a bakery and try to order pineapple buns in Chinese, although usually I just point to what I want. Or I'll sit in a wonton house with the smell of barbecued pork and Shanghai noodles, and listen in on the conversations around me. I don't know why, but the waitresses always greet me in English. I guess they can tell.

GLOSSARY

inkling   a hint
synonymous   the same, or almost the same
tucked away   put in a small place, not really noticeable
vegetarian diet   without meat
wonton house   a Chinese restaurant selling wontons made of boiled or fried
   dough filled with pork and spices

A CLOSER READING

1. Describe the mother as presented in the first three paragraphs. Describe the daughter. Do they get along well? Why might they have a problem getting along?

2. Describe the Shun-Wai of the grandparents. Is it a typical Shun-Wai? Why would her mother feel she has to take it apart?

3. The narrator went to Hong Kong when she was thirteen years old. What does she remember? Do you think it is the same picture that her mother had? Her grandparents? Tourists?

4. The narrator says *"Hong Kong made me realize I was Chinese."* What does she mean?

5. When her mother says grace, how do the family members react? Why? What does the mother mean when she says *"And forgive those who have turned their backs to you, Lord"*?

6. Why was Hong Kong "another culture"? What is the young woman's culture? What is the mother's culture?

7. With whom does the author want us to sympathize? Explain.

8. Why do the waitresses greet the narrator in English? What is it they "can tell"?

CULTURAL DISCUSSION

1. Why do the mother's, daughter's, and grandparents' perceptions of Hong Kong differ?

2. From what you know about Canadian culture, is the mother adapting to that culture? How do you think the grandparents feel? What might they say when their daughter leaves? Is their daughter a "gwua-mui"?

3. Irony means the opposite of what you would expect. Where is the irony in this story?

4. Should children try to become like others in a new country? Should they keep the identity that comes from their families?

5. Traditionally, the Canadian system has encouraged people to be self-supporting and to make their own decisions. Parents have raised their children to be independent. How do they do this? Are there any problems with the Canadian practise of wanting children to become independent as adults? Explain.

LOOKING AT LANGUAGE

Reading Between the Lines

Inference

When we read we get information. From this information we make *inferences* (conclusions) which are not stated in the text. Sometimes this is called "reading between the lines". For example, in "Shun-Wai" the narrator says she and her mother *"aren't often on speaking terms"*. But because she tells us positive things about how her mother has taken care of herself, we can infer (conclude) that she cares about her mother and does not blame her for all the trouble between them. Another example of inference occurs when the narrator says her grandparents' shrine was *"tucked away in a space on a bookshelf"*. We infer that the grandparents were trying not to call attention to the shrine.

What inferences can be made about the following topics?

- the narrator's religion
- the aunt and uncle's religion
- the birthplace of the narrator
- why the narrator visits the wonton house
- why the waitresses greet the narrator in English

Connotation

This story probably had few words that you did not understand. You knew what the words *denoted* (dictionary meaning). However, words have a *connotation* as well;

they carry the suggestion of something that is positive or negative. For example, the words "illness" and "death" have a clear dictionary meaning, but they also have negative connotations. Words like "lightness" and "air" carry positive connotations.

Some words have different connotations in different languages. For example, "dragons" has a negative (frightening) image in the folklore of some cultures, but in China dragons are a symbol of good luck. Colours have different connotations in different cultures. In China, red is associated with weddings and white with funerals; in North America traditional brides wear white while red is the colour for Christmas and Valentine's Day. Therefore, the colours white and red will produce different images in China and in Canada.

Decide whether the following words describing a person have a positive or negative connotation, or both. Would most Canadians agree or disagree?

1.	young	2.	old	3.	winner
4.	ambitious	5.	clean	6.	dreamy
7.	creative	8.	artistic	9.	imaginative
10.	a lie	11.	borrowing	12.	lending
13.	fighting	14.	giving advice		

Occasionally, someone more familiar with English cultures may need to help you figure out the connotation of a word. You may also be asked by others to explain connotations of words in your first language. Even among people from the same culture, the connotation of words can be different. For instance, the neutral term "vegetarian diet" has a different connotation for different people. It appears as a positive thing to the narrator of "Shun-Wai" but a negative thing to her mother.

What is the denotation of "Jesus"? What connotation does "Jesus" have for the narrator? For her mother?

Irony

An *ironic statement* means the opposite of what was said. "You're so funny" can mean "you are not funny at all". Sometimes people do not know there is irony in their actions. In this story, it is ironic that the mother's criticism of her daughter rejecting her Christian upbringing is not really different from her own rejection of her parents' religious practices.

In "Penny in the Dust", it is ironic that the boy and the father love each other but continuously misunderstand each other's feelings. The irony in literature reflects the many ironies in life.

What other instances of irony can you find in "Shun-Wai"?

Sarcasm

In "Shun-Wai" the narrator is mildly sarcastic when she talks about her mother's turning to Jesus. We can infer that the narrator does not believe in Jesus the way her mother does. *Sarcasm* involves a sharp comment that makes fun of, or is critical of, something or someone. For example, when the narrator says *"which is probably why she turned to Jesus"*, she is making fun of herself.

Sometimes sarcasm is hurtful, but in "Shun-Wai" the tone of the narrator's speech is not unkind. What do you think of the narrator? Is she disrespectful towards her mother?

Ambiguity

A statement that is *ambiguous* can be understood in more than one way. Often feelings are ambiguous; immigrants can be glad to settle in Canada but can be unhappy to be far from their families. Actions, as well as feelings, can be ambiguous. In "Shun-Wai", are the narrator's actions or feelings ambiguous?

REINFORCING SKILLS

1. Look at "The Other Family" and decide if any actions of the characters are ambiguous.
2. Paraphrase the main idea of "Shun-Wai".

ACTIVITIES

Essay Writing

1. Write a short essay describing the daughter's, the mother's and the grandparents' attitudes toward their religious traditions.
2. Write a short essay describing the cultural dilemma of the protagonist (the young woman).

THE MOOSE AND THE SPARROW

HUGH GARNER
(1913-1979)

Hugh Garner was born in England and came to Toronto in 1919. His family lived in a poor area of the city and he worked at many jobs to earn a living. He published many novels and short story collections and, in 1963, won a Governor General's Award for Hugh Garner's Best Stories. *"The Moose and the Sparrow" is from* Men and Women, *published in 1966. His best-known work is* Cabbagetown, *a novel about a working-class neighbourhood in Toronto.*

PREPARING TO READ

This is a story about lumberjacks in British Columbia and a university student who joins their camp for summer employment. What do loggers do? What do you think is the atmosphere in a logging camp? Do you think a university student will do well there? What would you predict might happen in that logging camp?

Hugh Garner uses the specialized language of the logging industry to make us feel we are in the camp watching this story unfold. Although these terms add to the authentic flavour, it is not necessary to understand every new term. Knowing what the setting is, you can simply follow the plot and look more closely at these terms later.

From the very beginning Moose Maddon picked on him. The kid was bait for all of Maddon's cruel practical jokes around the camp. He was sent back to the tool-house for left-handed saws, and down to the office to ask the pay cheater if the day's mail was in, though the rest of us knew it was only flown out every week.

The kid's name was Cecil, and Maddon used to mouth it with a simpering mockery, as if it pointed to the kid being something less than a man. I must admit though that the name fitted him, for Cecil was the least likely lumberjack I've seen in over twenty-five years in lumber camps. Though we knew he was intelligent enough, and a man too, if smaller than most of us, we all kidded him, in the good-natured way a bunkhouse gang will. Maddon however always lisped the kid's name.

Moose Maddon was as different from Cecil as it is possible for two human beings to be and still stay within the species. He was a big moose of a man, even for a lumber stiff, with a round flat unshaven face that looked down angrily and dourly at the world. Cecil on the other hand was hardly taller than an axe handle, and almost as thin. He was about nineteen years old, with the looks of an inquisitive sparrow behind his thick horn-rimmed glasses. He had been sent out to the camp for the summer months by a distant relative who had a connection with the head office down in Vancouver.

That summer we were cutting big stuff in an almost inaccessible stand of Douglas fir about fifty miles out of Nanaimo. The logs were catted five miles down to the river where they were bunked waiting for the drive. Cecil had signed on as a whistle punk, but after a few days of snarling the operation with wrong signals at the wrong time and threatening to hang the rigging-slingers in their own chokers, he was transferred to Maddon's gang as a general handyman. Besides going on all the ridiculous and fruitless errands for Moose, he carried the noon grub to the gangs from the panel truck that brought it out from camp, made the tea and took the saws and axes in to old Bobbins, the squint eye, to be sharpened.

For the first two weeks after he arrived, the jokes were the usual ones practised on a greenhorn, but when they seemed to be having little or no effect on his bumbling habits and even temper Moose devised more cruel and intricate ones. One night Moose and a cohort of his called Lefevre carried the sleeping Cecil, mattress and all, down to the river and threw him in. The kid almost drowned, but when he had crawled up on shore and regained his breath he merely smiled at his tormentors and ran back to the bunkhouse, where he sat shivering in a blanket on the springs of his bunk till the sun came up.

Another time Moose painted a wide moustache with tar on Cecil's face while he slept. It took him nearly a week to get it all off, and his upper lip was red and sore-looking for longer than that.

Nearly all of us joined in the jokes on Cecil at first, putting a young raccoon in his bunk, kicking over his tea water, hiding his clothes or tying them in knots, all the usual things. It wasn't long though until the other men noticed that Moose Maddon's jokes seemed to have a grim purpose. You could almost say he was carrying out a personal vendetta against the kid for refusing to knuckle under or cry "Uncle". From then on everybody but Moose let the kid alone.

One evening as a few of us sat outside the bunkhouse shooting the guff, Moose said, "Hey, Cecil dear, what do you do over on the mainland?"

"Go to school," Cecil answered.

Moose guffawed. "Go to school? At your age?"

Cecil just grinned.

"What school d'ya go to, Cecil? Kindergarten?" Moose asked him, guffawing some more.

"No."

"You afraid to tell us?"

"No."

"Well, what school d'ya go to?"

"U.B.C."

"What's that, a hairdressin' school?"

"No, the university."

"University! You!"

Moose, who was probably a Grade Four dropout himself, was flabbergasted. I'm sure that up until that minute he'd been living in awe of anybody with a college education.

"What you takin' up?" he asked, his face angry and serious now.

"Just an arts course," Cecil said.

"You mean paintin' pictures an' things?"

"No, not quite," the kid answered.

For once Moose had nothing further to say.

From then on things became pretty serious as far as Moose and Cecil were concerned. On at least two occasions the other men on the gang had to prevent Moose from beating the boy up, and old Bobbins even went so far as to ask Mr. Semple, the walking boss, to transfer the youngster to another gang. Since learning that Cecil was a college boy, Moose gave him no peace at all, making him do jobs that would have taxed the strength of any man in the camp, and cursing him out when he was unable to do them, or do them fast enough.

The kid may not have been an artist, as Moose had thought, but he could make beautiful things out of wire. Late in the evenings he would sit on his bunk and fashion belt-buckles, rings and tie-clips from a spool of fine copper wire he'd found in the tool shed. He made things for several of the men, always refusing payment for them. He used to say it gave him something to do, since he couldn't afford to join in the poker games.

One evening late in the summer as I was walking along the river having an after-supper pipe, I stumbled upon Cecil curled up on a narrow sandy beach.

His head was buried in his arms and his shoulders were heaving with sobs. I wanted to turn around without letting him know he'd been seen, but he looked so lonely crying there by himself that I walked over and tapped him on the shoulder.

He jumped as if I'd prodded him with a peavey, and swung around, his eyes near-ly popping from his head with fright. The six weeks he'd spent working under Moose Maddon hadn't done his nerves any good.

"It's all right, kid," I said.

"Oh! Oh, it's you, Mr. Anderson!"

He was the only person in camp who ever called me anything but "Pop".

"I don't mean to butt in," I said. "I was just walking along here, and couldn't help seeing you. Are you in trouble?"

He wiped his eyes on his sleeve before answering me. Then he turned and stared out across the river.

"This is the first time I broke down," he said, wiping his glasses.

"Is it Moose?"

"Yes."

"What's he done to you now?"

"Nothing more than he's been doing to me all along. At first I took it—you know that, Mr. Anderson, don't you?"

I nodded.

"I thought that after I was out here a couple of weeks it would stop," he said. "I expected the jokes that were played on me at first. After all I was pretty green when I arrived here. When they got to know me the other men stopped, but not that—that Moose."

He seemed to have a hard time mouthing the other's name.

"When are you going back to school?" I asked him.

"In another couple of weeks."

"Do you think you can stand it until then?"

"I need all the money I can make, but it's going to be tough."

I sat down on the sand beside him and asked him to tell me about himself. For the next ten or fifteen minutes he poured out the story of his life; he was one of those kids who are kicked around from birth. His mother and father had split up while he was still a baby, and he'd been brought up in a series of foster homes. He'd been smart enough, though, to graduate from high school at seventeen. By a miracle of hard work and self-denial he'd managed to put himself through the first year of university, and his ambition was to continue on to law school. The money he earned from his summer work here at the camp was to go towards his next year's tuition.

When he finished we sat in silence for a while. Then he asked, "Tell me, Mr. Anderson, why does Maddon pick on me like he does?"

I thought about his question for a long time before answering it. Finally I said, "I guess that deep down Moose knows you are smarter than he is in a lot of ways. I guess he's—well, I guess you might say he's jealous of you."

"No matter what I do, or how hard I try to please him, it's no good."

"It never is," I said.

"How do you mean?"

I had to think even longer this time. "There are some men, like Moose Maddon, who are so twisted inside that they want to take it out on the world. They feel that most other men have had better breaks than they've had, and it rankles inside them. They try to get rid of this feeling by working it out on somebody who's even weaker than they are. Once they pick on you there's no way of stopping them short of getting out of their way or beating it out of their hide."

Cecil gave me a wry grin. "I'd never be able to beat it out of the—the Moose's hide."

"Then try to keep out of his way."

"I can't for another two weeks," he said. "I'm afraid that before then he'll have really hurt me."

I laughed to reassure him, but I was afraid of the same thing myself. I knew that Moose was capable of going to almost any lengths to prevent Cecil leaving the camp without knuckling under at least once; his urge seemed to me to be almost insane. I decided to talk to George Semple myself in the morning, and have the boy flown out on the next plane.

"I don't think Moose would go so far as to really hurt you," I told him.

"Yes he would! He would, Mr. Anderson, I know it! I've seen the way he's changed. All he thinks about any more are ways to make me crawl. It's no longer a case of practical jokes; he wants to kill me!"

My reassuring laugh stuck in my throat this time. "In another two weeks, son, you'll be back in Vancouver, and all this will seem like a bad dream."

"He'll make sure I leave here crippled," Cecil said.

We walked back to the camp together, and I managed to calm him down some.

The next day I spoke to Semple, the walking boss, and convinced him we should get the boy out of there. There was never any thought of getting rid of Moose, of course. Saw bosses were worth their weight in gold, and the top brass were calling for more and more production all the time. Whatever else Moose was, he was the best production foreman in the camp. When Semple spoke to Cecil, however, the kid refused to leave. He said he'd made up his mind to stick it out until his time was up.

Though my gang was working on a different side than Maddon's, I tried to keep my eye on the boy from then on. For a week things went on pretty much as usual, then one suppertime Cecil came into the dining hall without his glasses. Somebody asked him what had happened, and he said there'd been an accident, and that Moose had stepped on them. We all knew how much of an accident it had been; luckily the kid had an old spare pair in his kit. Few of his gang had a good word for Moose any more, which only seemed to make him more determined to take his spite out on the kid.

That evening I watched Cecil fashioning a signet ring for one of the men out of wire and a piece of quartz the man had found. The way he braided the thin wire and shaped it around a length of thin sapling was an interesting thing to see. Moose was watching him too, but pretending not to. You could see he hated the idea of Cecil getting along so well with the other men.

"I was going to ask you to make me a new watch strap before you left," I said to Cecil. "But it looks like you're running out of wire."

The kid looked up. "I still have about twenty-five feet of it left," he said. That'll be enough for what I have in mind. Don't worry, Mr. Anderson, I'll make you the watch strap before I leave."

The next afternoon there was quite a commotion over where Maddon's gang were cutting, but I had to wait until the whistle blew to find out what had happened. Cecil sat down to supper with his right hand heavily bandaged.

"What happened?" I asked one of Maddon's men.

"Moose burned the kid's hand," he told me. "He heated the end of a saw blade in the tea fire, and then called the kid to take it to the squint eye to be sharpened. He handed the hot end to Cecil, and it burned his hand pretty bad."

"But—didn't any of you—?"

"None of us was around at the time. When we found out, big Chief went after Moose with a cant hook, but the rest of us held him back. He would have killed Moose. If Maddon doesn't leave the kid alone, one of us is going to have to cripple him for sure."

Moose had been lucky that The Chief, a giant Indian called Danny Corbett, hadn't caught him. I made up my mind to have Cecil flown out in the morning without fail, no matter how much he protested.

That evening the kid turned in early, and we made sure there was always one of us in the bunkhouse to keep him from being bothered by anybody. He refused to talk about the hand-burning incident at all, but turned his head to the wall when anybody tried to question him about it. Moose left shortly after supper to drink and play poker in Camp Three, about a mile away through the woods.

I woke up during the night to hear a man laughing near the edge of the camp, and Maddon's name being called. I figured it was Moose and Lefevre coming home drunk from Camp Three, where the bull cook bootlegged homebrew.

When I got up in the morning, Cecil was already awake and dressed, sitting on the edge of his bunk plaiting a long length of his copper wire, using his good hand and the ends of the fingers of the one that was burned.

"What are you doing up so early?" I asked him.

"I went to bed right after chow last night, so I couldn't sleep once it got light." He pointed to the plaited wire. "This is going to be your watch strap."

"But you didn't need to make it now, Cecil," I said. "Not with your hand bandaged and everything."

"It's all right, Mr. Anderson," he assured me. "I can manage it okay, and I want to get it done as soon as I can."

Just as the whistle blew after breakfast one of the jacks from Camp Three came running into the clearing shouting that Moose Maddon's body was lying at the bottom of a deep narrow ravine outside the camp. This ravine was crossed by means of a fallen log, and Moose must have lost his footing on it coming home drunk during the night. There was a free fall of more than forty feet down to a rocky stream bed.

None of us were exactly broken-hearted about Moose kicking off that way, but the unexpectedness of it shocked us. We all ran to the spot, and the boys rigged a sling from draglines and hauled the body to the top of the ravine. I asked Lefevre if he'd been with Moose the night before, but he told me he hadn't gone over to Camp Three. Later in the day the district coroner flew out from Campbell River or somewhere, and after inspecting the log bridge made us rig a handline along it. He made out a certificate of accidental death.

When they flew the body out, Cecil stood with the rest of us on the river bank, watching the plane take off. If I'd been in his place I'd probably have been cheering, but he showed no emotion at all, not relief, happiness, or anything else.

He worked on my watch strap that evening, and finished it the next day, fastening it to my watch and attaching my old buckle to it. It looked like a real professional job, but when I tried to pay him for it he waved the money aside.

It was another week before Cecil packed his things to leave. His hand had begun to heal up nicely, and he was already beginning to lose the nervous twitches he'd had while Moose was living. When he was rowed out to the company plane, all the boys from his bunkhouse were on the river bank to see him go. The last we saw of Cecil was his little sparrow smile, and his hand waving to us from the window.

One day in the fall I went out to the ravine to see how the handline was making it. It still shocked me to think that Maddon, who had been as sure-footed as a chipmunk, and our best man in a log-rolling contest, had fallen to his death the way he had. Only then did I notice something nobody had looked for before. In the bark of the trunks of two small trees that face each other diagonally across the fallen log were burn marks that could have been made by wire loops. A length of thin wire rigged from one to the other would have crossed the makeshift footbridge just high enough to catch a running man on the shin, and throw him into the ravine. Maddon could have been running across the log that night, if he'd been goaded by the laughter and taunts of somebody waiting at the other end. I remembered the sound of laughter and the shouting of Maddon's name.

I'm not saying that's what happened, you understand, and for all I know nobody was wandering around outside the bunkhouses on the night of Maddon's death, not Cecil or anybody else. Still, it gives me a queer feeling sometimes, even yet, to look down at my wrist. For all I know I may be the only man in the world wearing the evidence of a murder as a wristwatch strap.

GLOSSARY

bait   (*metaphorical*) food placed in a trap
bootlegged   sold illegal homemade liquor
dourly   overly serious
greenhorn   new worker
handyman   person who does many different small jobs

horn-rimmed   with the shape of an owl's eye
kindergarten   preschool, age four or five
knuckle under   (*idiom*) to give in
lisped   a speech problem when /s/ and /z/ sound like /th/
mockery   imitating with silliness or cruelty
pay cheater   person who handles the money in a camp
peavey   a pointed stick with a hook, used for moving logs
poker   a game of cards that usually involves betting money
shooting the guff   (*idiom*) casually chatting
signet   like a seal (device for making an impression on wax, formerly used to prove
   authenticity)
simpering   smiling in a silly way
snarling   mixing up
threatening to hang the rigging slingers   unintentionally coming close to
   killing the men who are up in the tree sawing it
to cry 'uncle'   (*idiom*) to plead for mercy
vendetta   a continuous fight between two groups or individuals who take turns
   trying to kill each other
walking boss and saw boss   names of logging supervisors
whistle punk   gives signals to lumberjacks when the trees they are cutting are
   ready to fall

A CLOSER READING

1.   What is the problem, as described in the first two paragraphs? Who is the narrator?
2.   What is Cecil's job?
3.   Why does Cecil annoy Moose? What kinds of things does Moose do to Cecil? Do others join in the teasing?
4.   When do the other men decide to leave Cecil alone?
5.   Why does the situation worsen when Moose learns that Cecil is a university student?
6.   What artistic talent does Cecil have? How does he use his talent? What do you think Moose thinks of this talent?
7.   Paraphrase Mr. Anderson's conversation with Cecil. What is Mr. Anderson like? What is Cecil like? What advice does Mr. Anderson give Cecil? Does Cecil take the advice?
8.   What did you think Cecil was referring to when he says twenty-five feet "will be enough for what I have in mind"? Were you correct?

9. Tell, in sequence, what happens after Moose burns Cecil's hand? What does Mr. Anderson hear that night? Why doesn't he tell the police? Why doesn't Cecil show any emotion when they take Moose's body out by plane?

10. What does Mr. Anderson find at the ravine the next fall? Why doesn't he tell the police?

11. What do you think happened?

12. Does the outcome of the story change your opinion about what Cecil is like? What does the title, "The Moose and the Sparrow", mean? Is Cecil like a sparrow (notice the metaphor)?

CULTURAL DISCUSSION

1. Moose and Cecil come from different backgrounds. Explain. Do different backgrounds mean that two people will not get along?

2. Could Cecil have handled the situation differently? How about Mr. Anderson? Is this kind of violence ever justified? Some cultures have "rules" for reacting to violence, for example, to "turn the other cheek" (do not fight back) or vengeance (a life for a life). What "rule" do you think exists in Canada, in theory and in practice? Is this a written rule?

3. How do people of different backgrounds (cultures) get along with each other in Canada? Explain.

4. What advice would you give your children on how to
   a. respond to a bully?
   b. respond to prejudice?
   c. get along with people who are different from themselves?

5. Does Cecil have any friends in the camp? Explain. What is a friend?

6. What would you have done if you were Cecil?

7. If you were Mr. Anderson, would you have told the police what you suspected? Why or why not?

8. Rewrite the end of the story as if Cecil had finally "knuckled under" to Moose.

LOOKING AT LANGUAGE

Synonyms

One way to remember new vocabulary is to keep a list of nouns, verbs, adjectives and adverbs with their *synonyms* (words of similar meaning). Use a dictionary and a thesaurus for the following words from this story. (Remember to first determine each word's part of speech in the sentence so that you find the right definition in the dictionary. The abbreviations are "n." for noun, "v.i." and "v.t." for verb intransitive and verb transitive, "adj." for adjective, and "adv." for adverb.)

	noun	verb	adjective	adverb	synonym
bully	x				tormentor
bait					
mockery					
inquisitive					
inaccessible					
grim					

Homonyms

Some words look alike but mean something different; for example, "snarling" in this story is a verb meaning "to mix two things up". But "snarling" is also an adjective meaning something which makes threatening noises. How many words can you think of which look alike and mean something different (you can include words which can change into another part of speech, such as "cry" (v.) which can also be a noun).

REINFORCING SKILLS

1. Define these words with the help of the story's context:
   a. species   b. grub   c. cohort
   d. even temper   e. guffawed   f. flabbergasted
   g. green (*metaphor*)   h. rankles

2. Do the following words have a positive, negative or neutral connotation in this story? Could they have a different connotation in another context?
   a. Moose   b. Sparrow   c. green

ACTIVITIES

Essay Writing

1. Write an essay contrasting Moose and Cecil and explain why they do not get along.

2. Write an essay agreeing or disagreeing with Cecil's response to Moose's first teasing and jokes. Use the text for your description of the response and give reasons for your agreement or disagreement.

LIFEGUARD
BARBARA J. SCOTT
(b. 1957)

Barbara Scott was born in Saskatoon, Saskatchewan, in 1957. Her stories have been published in various Canadian magazines. She experiments with narrator voice, as in this story, "Lifeguard", told in the voice of a sixteen-year-old boy. In addition to writing stories, she has taught English at the Alberta College of Art and the University of Calgary.

PREPARING TO READ

This story is told from the viewpoint of a sixteen-year-old boy whose parents have separated. His mother has moved to Vancouver to get a better job but the boy has remained in an unnamed city, probably in Alberta, where he works as a lifeguard.

Can you predict what could happen to this boy? Is he old enough to be on his own? Could this situation occur in the place where you grew up? What is the age when most boys mature? And girls?

The language of this story is *colloquial* (like conversation rather than the written word) and includes words that are considered rude by some people.

I don't usually hold much with small kids. That might seem kind of strange coming from a lifeguard at the Bridgeland Community swimming pool, but the job gives me free pool time, and I'm training for the city tryouts. Keeping snot-nosed kids from drowning themselves and one another is the only price I have to pay. Besides, I had my own problems that summer.

I came down hard on the little buggers the first couple of weeks, which was enough to drive off most of them, but Mike was different. Man, that kid stuck to me like a leech no matter how hard I tried to shake him loose. Time and again I'd tell him teaching swimming techniques wasn't part of my job, but he'd still be after me, "How's my crawl doin' Chris?" and "Watch me do the butterfly." So just to get some peace I'd watch him thrash his way around the shallow end of the pool. He was lousy, but no amount of telling him so would get him off my back.

Mike was so scrawny he barely had enough ass to hang swim trunks on, and without his glasses, his eyes were always slightly out of focus, like he was looking at something just beyond you. For all the times I saw him at the pool, I don't think I ever saw him swim with anybody—he was always off by himself, puffing and blowing like a baby whale. His mom would drop him off at the gate. (She looked a bit like my mom. First time I saw her I thought for a minute Mom had changed her mind about taking the job in Vancouver, about taking my kid brother with her.) After his mom left, Mike'd spend all his time paddling in the shallow end. And bugging me. Like I didn't have better things to do with my time.

One day he scared the hell out of me. I hadn't taken my eyes off the pool for more than a few minutes. I was just checking out one of the babes that hangs out at the pool in a bathing suit that's a clear signal she ain't there for the swimming. All of a sudden I see Mike splashing around in the deep end of the pool. So I'm in the pool like a flash, hauling him to the surface and throwing him onto the edge like a dead mackerel, cursing through the water that's splashing into my mouth. "You dumb little shit! What do you think you're doing down in this end of the pool! You could've drowned!"

He stands there streaming with water and just looks at me with this weird, shining kind of look.

"Wow! That is so cool!"

I poke him in the chest, hard. "Cut the crap, man. What the hell were you doing down in the deep end?"

"You gotta try it, Chris."

"Try what?" The little snot had gone off the deep end in more ways than one.

"Look, I'll show you." And he starts off back to where I'd just finished hauling him out. Some people you have to hit over the head with a sledge hammer. I yanked him back by the arm.

"Haven't you heard a word I've been saying? You're not allowed down there unless you can swim a length."

"Why should I have to swim a length?" the kid asks. "Anybody can figure out that even if you fall in in the middle of the pool, the most you'd have to swim is half a width."

"Yeah, well, for you that'd still be pushing it."

"If I swim the width, will you let me show you?"

"Show me what?"

He answered with the kind of patience you'd show someone who wasn't wrapped too tight. "If I have to show you, I obviously can't tell you, can I?" And then before I can say anything, in he dives—into the deep end again, couldn't prove his point in the *shallow* end, not Mike. Well, he's moving like an egg-beater, churning up the water and looking like he'll go down any minute. But I have to admit that he's made it when he comes back up to me.

"Now watch," he says, like he's going to open me up to some kind of miracle.

What I see convinces me that the little squirt is definitely a little bent. He crouches down at the edge of the pool and wraps himself up like a cannonball, then slowly tips himself off the edge backwards, sort of unfolding as he sinks deeper and deeper into the water. I keep waiting for some kind of trick, but he just does a limp dead-man's float underneath the surface of the water, not moving, only kind of *wafting* like a fleshy seaweed. The longer he stays there the more nervous I get, and I'm starting to think I'm going to have to get wet a second time, when he slowly starts to move to the surface, bursting through near the ladder. He comes running up to me with the same goofy expression, like a pup that figures it's been really clever, "Did you see, Chris? Did you see?"

"See *what*?" He stares at me like *I'm* the moron.

"It's like... like falling into a... a cloud that stretches forever, and it just sort of wraps around you..." I tap my forehead with one finger and draw circles in the air. Mike's voice fizzles, "I guess you have to do it yourself to figure it out." He tugs at my finger. "Why don't you try it, Chris? It feels really neat."

"I have to get back to work, kid. I can't stand around all day listening to weirdos." I start to walk away. But he's a persistent guy, and you gotta admit that he doesn't take an insult. He just tags along, saying, "Yeah, but you will try it, won't you Chris?"

"Yeah, yeah, sure, kid." I keep walking.

I never did try it, sounded crazy to me. But Mike was at it lots over the summer. He was there almost every day, not swimming, just playing his strange little game. I was spending every spare minute at the pool, even helping to clean up after the last Belly-Burner Aquasize Class ended at eleven, just to put off going home. I boarded with an old couple who lived near the pool. They said I could have the run of the house, but they gave me the creeps, shuffling around and wheezing all the time. The whole place smelled of them. So I'd leave early in the morning and spend hours swimming lengths, cutting through the water's resistance like it was a personal enemy. My time improved, but at the end of one of those sessions I could barely stand.

Mom phoned every Sunday to see how I was doing and to cry and remind me that none of this was her fault, that the Vancouver job paid almost twice as much as her old job and if Dad hadn't run off like he did everything would be just peachy. But once she figured out I wasn't mad at her, she perked up and I started to look forward to the calls. Every Saturday night I'd be ready to say that I'd been wrong. Sixteen isn't old enough to look after yourself. Send me an airline ticket. But by Sunday I'd remember that I was practically a shoo-in for the city team. So we'd have one of those, "How're you doing?" "Just fine," conversations that last two minutes. Another two minutes with the kid bro and then a whole week filled with all the things I didn't say.

So I didn't notice exactly when Mike stopped coming to the pool. But one day I overheard a couple of parents talking while their kids were getting showered. Talking about Mike's family, talking in that hush-hush, greedy voice people take on when they go over gory details. Mike and his parents had been driving up to Saskatchewan to see some relatives. Just out of Drumheller they'd been hit head on by a kid out joy-riding, playing chicken with another guy. Asshole pulled out to pass on a curve and hit Mike's family doing about a hundred kliks. His buddy didn't even stop, but a passing Greyhound radioed the police. When they got there Mike's mom was squashed like an accordion under the dashboard and his dad was walking in big crazy circles all over the road, muttering to himself in gibberish and flapping his arms like a chicken. Mike had crawled into the corner farthest from his mom in the back seat and was staring from behind his shattered glasses, from one parent to the other, folded in on himself like a tight, hard ball.

Well, the pool is right near the hospital they had Mike at, so I went over to see him after work. I talked to a nurse there, and she filled me in on the rest of the story. Mike's mom was killed on impact, his dad took a few days more to go. They did a whole bunch of tests on Mike and apart from some cuts and a big bruise on his forehead, he was O.K. Physically.

Since they'd brought him in he hadn't said a word or looked like he could hear anyone else. They couldn't even tell if he knew his parents were dead. He didn't move, didn't speak, barely blinked. There wasn't a friend or a relative who could take him—he had to be dressed and changed like a baby—so they were sending him to a Home just a few blocks away.

I went up to his room and it was spooky the way he just sat there, staring at nothing. He didn't even look at me. I felt funny trying to talk to him, so I only stayed a few minutes that day. But the Home was even closer to the pool than the hospital, so I kind of got into the habit of dropping in on him every couple of days. He got on pretty well there. In a couple of weeks he was walking again and going to the toilet himself. But nobody could get a peep out of him. I almost gave up going, but I couldn't get him out of my head, he looked so scrawny and small behind his glasses. Once I missed seeing him for about five days. When I finally made it back, he looked at me. That was it, he didn't smile or look at me again the rest of the visit, but at least I knew he was in there somewhere. I started telling him all about the pool, how they were putting in a whirlpool for sports injury therapy, how the fall classes had started and I'd been hired as an instructor, how most of the kids were worse swimmers than he was and boy was that saying something. I'd talk my head off like an idiot in the hopes of getting one flicker of the eyes, and the flicker got more frequent until the day I said, "Look Mike, why don't you come to the pool some time. Would you like that?"

He touched my face with one finger.

Well, I was like a crazy man, running up to the nurse all excited, shouting my head off. And she was just as bad. So that was how he started coming to the pool again, only this time a volunteer attendant brought him. The guy would sit Mike in the shallow end and kind of play with him, splashing him lightly with water, letting him walk around. Mike seemed to be quite happy just to sit or paddle. He was tired and old-looking, too feeble to resist when the attendant steered him away from the deep end. I began to think that this might be the best he'd ever do.

Then one day, while the attendant was talking to one of the girls in the new jacuzzi, I see Mike head for the deep end, walking close to the edge, jerkily, like he's on automatic pilot. The deep end is near the jacuzzi and I figure it's only a matter of moments before the volunteer sees what the kid's up to and hauls him away, so I kind of casually wander over to the whirlpool and block his view. All the time I'm watching Mike out of the corner of my eye and trying to convince myself that if he starts to get into trouble I can get him out of it, but I'm still pretty nervous. How the hell do I know why he's off to that end of the pool, anyway. But another part of me, lower down, is drumming out this message over and over, telling him to go for it, go for it, and I don't even really know what I mean. Well, Mike gets to the deep end and sure enough, the attendant looks over my shoulder and freaks. He leaps out of the whirlpool as Mike crouches down, but I hold him back by one arm. "Leave him alone, man."

"Are you crazy," he says, "you're gonna get me sued."

"Fuck off," I say, eyes glued to the kid.

Mike tips himself backwards into the pool.

"Jesus H. Christ!" yells the volunteer and hurls himself toward the pool, only to come smack up against me. I'm ready to punch him out if he takes one more step toward that kid, so help me God. Mike is floating like a dead man, loose and motionless beneath the water. My heart is just thrashing the inside of my chest when I think of what could be happening if I'm wrong. The attendant is staring at me like I'm a murderer and I'm grunting with the strain of holding him back. Just as I'm ready to jump into the pool, cursing myself for an idiot, Mike's arms and legs start to move. He looks like he's feeling his way through some invisible tunnel (how he can hold his breath for that long would amaze me, only I've been matching him second for second), then he bursts through into the open air, climbs out of the pool and walks to the same spot, more confidently, almost eagerly. He tips himself backwards again, eyes closed.

My hands are still digging into the attendant's arms—he'll have a hell of a bruise and I think I've strained a muscle in my wrist. We both take our first breath and I let him go. "See," I say while he rubs the red spots, "it's just his game. He's okay. I'll watch him." We dance around a little, cause I've wounded the guy's pride, but basically he's cool.

I still spend a lot of time at the pool. City tryouts are next month. And like I promised, I watch Mike, every day, while he tips himself into the depths of that big fluffy cloud, or living pool or the hands of God or whatever it is he thinks in his bent little brain is there. But I'll tell you something. Every time I see him break water it's like some kind of underwater flower bursting into the sunlight, and I swear I can feel the touch of something warm on my face.

GLOSSARY

Belly-Burner Aquasize Class   (*colloquial*) exercise class in a pool
city team   swim team which will enter competitions
Home   convalescent home, for rest and recovery after illness
joy-riding   driving aimlessly, perhaps recklessly
kliks   kilometres or miles
swim a length   swim the length of the pool once
to go   (*colloquial idiom*) to die
wrapped too tight   much too tense

A CLOSER READING

1. As described in the first two paragraphs, what is the narrator's attitude toward children?
2. How does Chris describe Mike?
3. When Chris says that Mike's mother reminds him of his own mother, what is foreshadowed (a hint of something that is going to happen)?
4. What does Mike want Chris to see and do? Why does he want this? Does Chris understand Mike? Why does Mike like Chris?
5. Where does Chris live and what does he think of the couple he lives with? Is he a nice person? How does he feel about being on his own? What are his conversations with his mother and brother like? How does he feel about the separation?
6. What is Mike's "game"? Why do you think he likes that game?
7. What happens to Mike's parents? To Mike?
8. Why does Chris visit Mike in the hospital?
9. At first, what does Mike do at the pool? Later? Why does the attendant object to Mike's "game"?
10. What effect does Chris have on Mike? What effect does Mike have on Chris?

CULTURAL DISCUSSION

1. Did your prediction about the sixteen-year boy on his own prove to be true?
2. Does Chris seem like sixteen-year-olds in the place where you grew up? In Canada? Do you think a sixteen-year-old should be independent? Is independence a good ideal?

3. Is this story realistic (could it really happen)?
4. Is Mike going to get better? Do you believe that one person can cause another to get well?
5. What makes one person help another? Why do people sometimes not help?
6. Why is the story called "Lifeguard"? Is this word used literally (dictionary definition) or figuratively?
7. What idea or feeling (connotation) does the word "summertime" have for you? How about "sports"?
8. This is a story about a young man written by a woman. Can women write well about men? And men about women? Does this mean men and women can understand each other?

LOOKING AT LANGUAGE

Idiomatic Language and Slang

"Lifeguard" is written in the voice of a sixteen-year-old boy. The tone is *colloquial* (like conversation rather than writing) and full of expressions such as *hold much*, *kind of strange*, *kid*, and *man*. Not everyone uses these expressions, but words like them are part of the idiom of many young people.

The word *idiom* has at least two meanings:
   (1) the special character of speech, as in "the idiom of a teenager", and
   (2) an expression that has a meaning different from its parts (to drive off, to hang on to).

Slang is an extreme form of colloquialism. It can be ordinary words which mean new things (*man* as a greeting; *ass* as an insult) or it can be new words (*joy-riding*, *kliks*, *spooky*) which can change over time. It can take the form of impolite words (*asshole*, *shit*) which usually refer to bodily functions and can be shocking to some people. (The shock value is what makes them appealing to others, especially young people feeling rebellious.)

Sometimes colloquial language is quite metaphorical and colourful (*playing chicken*, *like a dead man*). Often you can guess the meanings either from the words themselves or from their context.

Informal English is sometimes part of the idiom of high school, college and university students, and can be confusing to ESL students who have learned more formal English. Although you may not want to use these words and phrases yourself, it is useful to figure out some of their meanings in order to carry on conversations. (Note, however, that slang expressions change quickly. Some of those in "Lifeguard", written in 1989, may already be out-of-date or no longer used.)

From the story's context, guess the meaning of the following colloquial words and phrases:

1. hold much	2. "kind of" strange
3. snot-nosed kids	4. price I have to pay
5. buggers	6. came down hard (*idiom*)
7. to drive off (*idiom*)	8. stuck to me (*idiom*)
9. like a leech (*simile*)	10. to shake loose (*idiom*)
11. to be after [me] (*idiom*)	12. off my back (*idiom*)
13. scrawny	14. ass
15. scared the hell out of me	16. babes
17. hang out	18. like a dead mackerel
19. shit	20. cool
21. cut the crap	22. snot
23. to be pushing it	24. like an egg beater (*simile*)
25. a little bent	26. like a cannonball (*simile*)
27. dead-man's float	28. wafting
29. like a fleshy seaweed	30. moron
31. tap my forehead... and draw circles in the air	32. neat
33. put off	34. the creeps
35. kid bro	36. playing chicken
37. spooky	38. got on
39. go for it	40. freaks
41. get me sued	42. fuck off
43. cool	44. like some kind of... flower

REINFORCING SKILLS

Retell this story from the viewpoint of the boy, Mike. Use either the first person "I" or the third person "he".

ACTIVITIES

Essay Writing

1. Write an essay describing Chris both before he meets Mike and after (at the end of the story). Include reasons why you think Chris has changed.

2. Write an essay commenting on the use of colloquial language in the story and tell whether you think it is effective or ineffective.

FOOD AND SPIRITS
BY BETH BRANT
(b. 1941)

Beth Brant is from Tyendinaga Mohawk Territory in Ontario, near the Bay of Quinte. She began writing at the age of 40 and has authored Mohawk Trail *and been the editor for* A Gathering of Spirit, *a collection of literature and art by native women. This story, "Food and Spirits", dedicated to her Dad, is from a collection of her stories called* Food and Spirits *(1991).*

PREPARING TO READ

This story is about an 80-year-old Mohawk man who travels alone from his Indian reserve in Canada to visit his granddaughters in Detroit, Michigan (just north of Windsor, Ontario). Do you think he will encounter any trouble on his journey? In native cultures, it is the grandfather's role to counsel the younger generation. What role do elderly people play in the place where you grew up? How old is "old"? What do you think "old" means?

Elijah Powless decided it was time to take a trip.

He was driven to the bus stop by his son and daughter-in-law who, at the last moment, asked again, "Are you sure you want to do this, Father?"

And for the tenth or twentieth time he answered, "I want to see my granddaughters in the city. They are women now, and before I die I want to see how they are doin'."

Daughter-in-law shook her head but refrained from saying the usual: "You're not going to die. You see the girls all the time when they come to visit." She just shook her head, worried about letting an eighty-year-old man ride on a bus for seven hours to go to a place he'd never been. A big city. A big city in the States. A big city with the reputation of being the murder capital of the world!

Elijah had no faith in what newspapers or TV knew about a city. His twin granddaughters lived there—that was enough for him to go on.

The twins, Alice and Annie, were thrilled but anxious about their grandfather's trip. They offered to pay for the train fare and had even investigated plane routes and prices, but Elijah was firm in his insistence on paying for the bus ride himself.

"I'll see more from a bus. It's October, it'll be real pretty to see the land from a bus window. Besides, I don't want the twins to put out their hard-earned money on my trip."

So the daughter-in-law and the son had dutifully packed the suitcase and said many prayers. Elijah had also determined that he would take a bag of whitefish, frozen and wrapped in newspaper, and a separate bag of fry bread because, as Elijah said, "They don't get this kind of food in Detroit. I'll just make sure they have enough to last a few days."

"Please be careful, Father," the daughter-in-law breathed in his ear as she hugged him good-bye.

Elijah promised to be careful, though he wondered what he would have to be careful of. He had lived a good life. He had survived residential school with his own language and esteem intact. He had survived the Great Depression with a wife and five children. He had nursed his wife through cancer and on to death. He'd lost two sons to the white world and the alcohol in it. His three remaining children had finished school, had gotten jobs. The son standing before him now was a carpenter in a union, had a good wife, had twin daughters who were a joy in Elijah's life. He had been sad when the twins moved to the States to work for the Indian Center there. He was surprised that they had left home, but the twins were surprising girls. They were women now, he reminded himself. Thirty years old, unmarried, and Annie had declared she was thinking about adopting a child. It would be nice, Elijah thought, to be a great-grandfather to Annie's child. That was partly the reason he was taking this trip. He had it in mind that those Natives down there would listen to a man like himself. In fact, he was sure of it.

Getting on the bus and finding a seat, he waved good-bye to his son and daughter-in-law. He remarked to the woman sitting next to him, "My children are unhappy that I'm taking a trip. They think I'm too old and I need to be careful."

The woman turned her wide, fresh face toward him and smiled. Her false teeth glowed. "These kids sure do like to worry, don't they? They can't imagine that we old-timers might want to have some fun too." She whispered to Elijah, "I'm going to Windsor to visit my boyfriend. My daughter is scandalized that a woman my age has a beau."

Elijah was scandalized too. "You are a handsome woman. How come you only got one?"

They were laughing as the bus pulled out of the terminal. Well, this is good, Elijah told himself. A good sign. Laughter at the beginning means laughter at the end.

Elijah was trying to figure out how the woman got her hair that shade of blue when she stuck out her hand. "My name is Shirley Abbott."

"Elijah Powless," he said, and shook her hand. "How'd you get your hair that shade of blue?"

Shirley put her hands up to her short, puffy hair. "It's a rinse. Supposed to bring out the highlights in white hair. Don't you like it?" Shirley looked worried.

"Oh yeah, I like it fine. Goes with your dress," and he pointed at the bright blue material. Shirley relaxed.

"I just retired from my job," Shirley said. "I was a schoolteacher. Powless... Powless. Is that a Mohawk name?"

"Yep. How'd you know?"

"My sister married a man from Six Nations. I guess I heard the name there. Maybe we're related!"

"Well, I never seen a Mohawk with blue hair, but then, I never seen a lot of things." Elijah shifted the sacks on his lap. "Whitefish from the Bay. You can't get this kind of fish in Detroit. I caught it myself. My twin granddaughters live there, in Detroit, but they don't fish. Too busy, I guess. And this fry bread was made by their mother." Taking a round slab out of the bag, he offered it to Shirley.

She took a bite and rolled her eyes heavenward to indicate her pleasure. "This is good bread, Elijah. My sister makes it, but not as good as this. You tell that daughter of yours that she is an excellent cook."

"She is a good cook. Guess you can tell," and he pointed to his round belly, straining against his white shirt. He had dressed very carefully for this trip. In addition to his white dress shirt, he had on the new brown corduroy pants with the cuff smartly turned up. He was wearing his turtle bolo tie and had gotten a fresh haircut just the day before. He ran his hand through his greying short hair. It felt good. He would look sharp for the twins.

He glanced at Shirley who was having a hard time keeping her eyes open. She smiled, "I guess I'll take a little nap. I was up most of the night, too excited to sleep."

"Well, you gotta be fresh for that boyfriend."

Shirley giggled and settled in her seat. She closed her eyes.

Elijah looked out the window. It was so pretty, the day. The trees were turning color, shedding their green and taking on red and gold. Elijah felt very content to be on this bus, riding to see his twins, looking out the window at the beautiful trees, the cornfields, the occasional hawk sitting on a fence post. The crows were having a good day in the fields. They swooped in a great body to scavenge among the corn.

Elijah looked around at the other passengers. He wondered where they were going, what they were going to do when they got there. "Curiosity killed the cat," his wife had always said. Elijah retorted that he wasn't a cat and *his* curiosity had kept him going this long. Edith. He missed her to this day. She was a good and pretty woman. The twins looked like her. That special look on their faces, a look of excitement, like each day was going to bring a surprise. Even when she was dying, Edith had that look on her face. Edith. Elijah fell asleep.

Elijah had a dream. He was getting off the bus and there was Annie, standing with a baby in her arms. Alice stood right alongside her holding another baby. He reached for the babies and they called out, "Great-grandfather!" He held the babies, and the twins said, "These are your great-grandchildren. Twins, like us!"

He woke up and looked at Shirley who was smiling at him.

"You must have had a pleasant dream. You were grinning and laughing like you got the present of your life."

"I did. I got twins from the twins."

As they traveled, Elijah and Shirley talked. He told her about Edith. She told him about her husband, Alan.

"He wasn't good like your Edith. He was never happy with what he had. Always looking for some ship to come in. He gambled away almost every cent we had. I eventually got smart and put my earnings where he couldn't get to it. We did not have a peaceful life together. When he died, my daughter said, 'Good riddance.' I know what she meant, but it worried me that this was how she felt about her father."

"Takes more than a name to make a father. Kids don't get choices like grownups do. Mother, father, they gotta take what they get. If someone don't act like a father, why should a child love him like a daddy? You shouldn't worry about what's over. You got any grandchildren?"

Shirley shook her head no. "But my daughter is a lovely girl. She's given me a lot of pleasure in my life. I never had to worry about her for a minute."

Elijah nodded and looked out the window again. "Look, Shirley, there's a hawk comin' in on that tree! See how he hunches up and tucks his neck in? You'd never know he was there, would you? Hawks never give up. They'll chase something down till they get it. They gotta eat. None of this goin' to the store and gettin' food already there. Hawks gotta work."

"Can you picture a hawk going to the supermarket and picking out its food?" Shirley laughed.

"Well, now you mention it, I can't see it. If we worked as hard as the hawk for our food, we might think twice about throwin' so much away."

Shirley sighed, "I know what you mean, Elijah. These kids today, they don't know what it's like to go hungry. They think everything grows at the supermarket."

"Lots of kids know what it's like to go hungry. You just ain't been around them. Edie and me, we used to get the kids to help in the garden. I took 'em all huntin' and fishin'. But sometimes we went hungry too. But one thing, none of them is a waster of food."

"Look Elijah, there's the sign for Windsor!"

Shirley got up to go to the washroom. She came back smelling like lilac perfume, her lipstick newly applied, her blue hair stiff as a board.

Elijah made his way to the washroom and came back to his seat marveling at how small the room was. "I've never seen anything like it. While I was washing my hands I thought I was going to fall in the toilet, it was so crowded in there."

Shirley gathered her things together and sat, hands folded on top of her purse. "It's been a pleasure to meet you, Elijah. You tell those twins to take good care of you, now. I hope you enjoy your vacation."

Elijah thanked Shirley and helped her to her feet. He waved good-bye and watched her get off the bus to meet her beau.

Going through customs, Elijah wondered if Alice and Annie had changed much from six months ago when he'd last seen them. Riding through the tunnel that connected Detroit to Windsor, he smiled at his foolishness. They weren't children who changed constantly. They were women now, pretty much settled into what they would look and be like.

Elijah got up when the bus stopped. As he walked down the aisle, he caught glimpses of cement and traffic. Claiming his suitcase, he looked around for the twins. He went inside the terminal and still couldn't see them. He waited, suitcase by his feet, bags in hand, and watched all the people. There were so many kinds here. Black, brown, shades in between. White faces moved around him. They were walking to the bus, from the bus, sitting in the waiting room. Faces eating food, running after children, reading the papers. Teenage boys lined up at machines where they seemed to be playing some kind of game on a screen in front of them. Security guards and police walked through the building, keeping their eyes on the teenagers.

"Is this like TV?" Elijah asked a tall young man with dark brown skin. The young man was wearing a jacket with *Nike* streaking across the front. In fact, Nike seemed to be the young man's name, for the name was on his pants, on his shoes, and emblazoned on the cap that perched on his high hair.

"This ain't TV. It's Pacman, man."

"How does it work?"

"You puts the money in here, then you gotta get all the ghosts that pop up. Ain't you never seen this before? Man, where you been?"

Elijah dug in his pockets for coins.

"Hey, man, you can't play with that kinda money. You needs American money." He looked at the old man and his disappointed face. "But here, don't worry none. See that place over there? You pays them some a your money and you gets back American. Here, I show you."

He took Elijah over to the booth that said American Exchange on its sign and showed him how to do it.

"Thank you, Nike. I should have done this before I left home. Too excited I guess. Excited about seein' my twin granddaughters. Maybe I'm gettin' old."

"Aw, don't worry about it. Hey, what you call me?"

"Nike."

The young man laughed, revealing a gap between his two front teeth. "My name ain't Nike. Anyways, it's Nik*eee*, not Nike. My name's Terrance. Terrance James," and he held out his hand for Elijah to shake. "Is somebody meetin' you? You shouldn't be wanderin' around, old man like yourself. What you got in them bags?"

"Whitefish from the Bay and some fry bread. Here, have a piece." Elijah pulled out a thick round and gave it to his new friend. "Sorry I got your name wrong. But how come you got that name on your clothes? Maybe you're wearin' somebody else's? My name's Elijah. Elijah Powless."

"No, man, these are my clothes. Nike's a brand name, like the company that makes 'em. You don't know that?" Terrance laughed. "Man, where you been?"

Elijah remarked as how he'd been in Tyendinaga and this was his first trip to Detroit and he wondered where his granddaughters were.

"That ain't right. Old man like yourself at the bus stop with nobody to meet him. That ain't right. You got a number for them girls? We could call them, tell them to get their butts over here to pick up their granddaddy. That ain't right."

Terrance pulled at his lip and looked worried while Elijah went through his pockets to find the number for their twins. "Here it is."

"There's the phone over there," Terrance pointed to the booth. "I'll wait here and play me some more games."

Elijah left his bags by Terrance, who assured him he'd keep an eye out for them. He dialed the number and let it ring ten times. He hung up the phone, wondering what to do next. Then he walked back.

"They ain't home," he said to Terrance. "I don't know what could be keepin' them, but I ain't worried. Now, show me how to play this game."

Terrance finished chewing the last piece of fry bread and showed Elijah where to put his quarters and how to play the Pacman game. "This is good bread. You got a whole bag of it? That all you got to eat?"

"No, I just brought it for the twins. You can't get this kinda food in Detroit. What kinda food *do* you get in Detroit?"

"Well, you can gets chicken or ribs or MacDonald's over there. But the best food is what my mama makes. Cornbread that'll melt in your mouth! Hey man, you Mexican or somethin'?" said Terrance, studying Elijah's face.

"I'm Mohawk. Indian."

"Yeah, we got somma them around here. They have a parade sometime. Me and my friends go. Somma them guys dance and wear these fancy costumes. Very impressive. My mama say that on my daddy's side, we gots Indian blood."

"Is that right? What kinda Indian? Is your daddy from around here?"

"My daddy ain't from around nowhere. He long dead and gone, I hopes. I don't know what kinda Indian. It's all the same," Terrance nodded sagely.

"Well, it ain't all the same. But then again," Elijah said, scratching his head, "maybe it is. You gotta point there, Terrance. You're a smart young man. You go to school?"

"Hell no! I ain't been in school for four years now. I quit when I was sixteen."

"Why'd you do that, a smart boy like yourself?"

"Hey man, I'm smart 'cause I ain't goin' to school. School ain't no place for Terrance James. Shit!"

"Maybe you were in the wrong school. Seems like you shoulda done real good in school." Elijah looked around the terminal. "I wonder where those twins are."

"What we gonna do, Elijah?"

"Play another game on this Pacman machine."

Terrance laughed and loaded up the quarters. They played three more games of Pacman before they noticed another man was making signals to Terrance. "I gotta go outside for a minute, Elijah. I'll tell you what. Across the street there's a bar. I know the dude who works there. They don't let you wait around here, unless you catchin' a bus. Why don't you go over there and wait. I be back here in a minute, just gotta little business to take care of. I'll wait on the twins and you can visit with Archibald. He the dude works across the street. It be alright there. He take care a you till them twins get here." Terrance shifted from one foot to the other.

"You in a hurry, Terrance? Here, take another piece of bread. I appreciate what you're doin'. Archibald, eh? I guess I am kinda thirsty. See you later."

Terrance smiled and hurried out after the man who was impatiently waiting.

Elijah stood for a few minutes, collecting his thoughts and belongings. He walked toward the door and looked out. There, across the street, just like Terrance said, was the place where he should go. FOOD & SPIRITS, the sign said.

He crossed the street, cars braking and horns blaring. A driver shouted out, "Watch where you're going, old man!"

Elijah waved and made it safely across the street and stood at the door where the FOOD & SPIRITS sign blinked on and off. He pushed on the door and went into the dark room. Music was playing from a jukebox in the corner. Two people turned to look at him when he entered the room.

Seeing the slim, dark man behind the bar, Elijah inquired, "Are you Archibald? Terrance James sent me here. Said you was a dude who'd look after me until my twins come to get me."

"I'm Archibald. What you want? What Terrance up to sendin' you here? I'll look after you, he say? Hummmpph." Archibald scratched his head, then continued to polish the glasses he had lined up in front of him.

"What does food and spirits mean? What kinda food you got here? What kinda spirits?" Elijah sat down on a stool, carefully placing his suitcase and parcels beside him.

Archibald polished the glasses, holding one up to the dim light, then polishing some more. "Just what it say. We got sandwiches, we got burgers, we got fries, we got drinks. What'll it be old-timer? And how'd you get my name from Terrance?" Archibald stared at Elijah. "Don't seem like nobody Terrance James would know."

"I met Terrance at the bus station. A smart young man. We played on the Pacman machine, and he told me his daddy was an Indian, like me."

"Hummmpph. What'll it be, old-timer?"

"Oh, I guess I'll have one of them pops. Ginger ale. I got some fry bread here. Have a piece."

Archibald looked suspiciously at the round hunk of bread offered to him. His brown eyes stared at Elijah. He shook his head no, his large Afro glinting from the light behind the bar. His dark brown skin reminded Elijah of the color of tea, nice and strong. Archibald's skin was smooth and unlined except for a scar running up his left eyebrow to his hairline. "One Vernor's comin' up."

He poured the ginger ale into a glass filled with ice. As he set it in front of Elijah he asked, "What kinda bread is that? Where you comin' from that you met Terrance at the bus? You waitin' on somebody?"

"This is fry bread, made by my daughter-in-law. I just come down from Tyendinaga. My twin granddaughters were supposed to meet me, but something seems to have held them up. Don't worry, they'll be here." Elijah took a long swallow from his glass. "Deeeelicious!"

"Oh, I ain't worryin'," Archibald stated. "It just seem you not the kinda man that Terrance would run with. Where's this Tidaga place?"

"Tyendinaga. It's an Indian place, very pretty. It's my home." He indicated the brown bag at his side. "I got whitefish here from the Bay. We eat a lot of it. I brought it for the twins 'cause they don't get this kinda food here."

"You got that right. You from a reservation, huh? I never met no Indian from a reservation. Give you a little rye to sweeten that ginger ale?"

Elijah held up his hands. "No, my drinkin' days are over. I'm eighty years old and stick with pop these days. So Archibald, my name is Elijah. Elijah Powless. What kinda spirits you got in this place?"

"Huh. The only kinda spirits what live here is whiskey spirit, gin spirit, and rum spirit. I'm pleased to meet you, Elijah." He held out his hand. "Maybe they be other spirits, too. I ain't taken inventory lately." Archibald laughed, and the woman sitting next to Elijah giggled.

"This here's Alana. Alana here's our spirit from the bus station. She hang out here when she ain't over there."

His eyes adjusted to the lack of light in the bar, Elijah turned to smile at the woman sitting next to him. She was smiling back, her bright pink lips opened over small, white teeth. Her skin was the color of unfinished pine, Elijah thought, and her hair was the blondest and curliest he'd ever seen. Curls were draped over her shoulders and tumbling down her back. She was wearing purple eye shadow that made her brown eyes look like wet silk. Two pink spots, the size of half dollars, were painted on her cheeks. Her black skirt was very short and kept sliding up her legs, revealing purple garters around her thighs. Elijah looked away, lest Alana think him impolite to be staring at those purple garters.

"Hey, Elijah, how you doin'?" Alana held out her fingers for Elijah to touch. "So you a real Indian, Elijah? My, my, I never met one before. Imagine, in this bar, I be sittin' next to a real Indian. My, my."

Elijah shook Alana's fingers and offered her a piece of fry bread.

"This look like fry cake, don't it Archibald? Fry cake like my grandmama used to make." She took a bite, and her face expressed delight. "This is so good! Elijah, what you doin' carryin' sacks a fry cake around town? What's them twins thinkin' of, lettin' you wander 'round this city with a bag of fry cakes? It ain't safe!"

"It ain't their fault, Alana. I don't know what could have happened to them. But I ain't worried, yet. Do you know my twins, Alice and Annie? My granddaughters. Very pretty girls. They look like their grandmother, my Edie."

"How come Edie ain't with you, 'Lijah?" Archibald asked.

"Oh, she's been dead a long time. Cancer."

"Terrible," Alana whispered. "My mama had cancer. She had a lot of pain. I hope Edie didn't have no pain like that!"

"She did. But the place Edie's at now, I know she's happy there. No pain, just pretty things to see and all her relatives hangin' out there. Right before she died, she took my hand and said, 'Elijah, it's beautiful. It's beautiful.' Then she died. Edie was a pretty woman, so I can't imagine that the spirit place wouldn't be too."

"Ain't that beautiful," Alana sighed.

"How come Archibald said you was the spirit of the bus stop, Alana?"

"Oh him! He teasin' you," Alana giggled. "I ain't no spirit. Just a workin' girl. I work over at the bus stop sometime. I works here sometime."

"What do you do? I was a janitor when I was younger," Elijah took another sip from his glass.

Alana looked at Elijah, her silk eyes widening. "Honey, I just told you I was a workin' girl. I work the streets. Hustle. Workin' girl, workin' girl! I'm the spirit of the workin' girls!"

Archibald laughed, a rich baritone rumble coming through his throat. "Then I must be the spirit-keeper. The keeper of all the spirits in this here bar!"

Elijah looked at Archibald. "I like that. The spirit-keeper of the bar. It suits you. You look like the keeper of the spirits."

Archibald checked his reflection in the mirror behind the bar. "Well, maybe. But here, have another pop on me. Alana? Another of the same?" He busied himself with getting fresh napkins and clean glasses.

Alana checked her watch. "I guess I could stand another. It gettin' cold out there."

The door opened and a white man in a suit walked in. His eyes roamed around the bar and settled on the three faces looking at him. He turned around and went out the door.

Archibald laughed. "He don't like the color of the spirits in this here bar!" They laughed together, Alana's high-pitched giggle floating above them.

"What spirit are you, Elijah? If I'm the spirit of the workin' girl, and Archibald here's the spirit-keeper, then what are you?"

Elijah thought and took another swallow of his pop. "I guess you could call me the old Indian spirit. Put me up on the shelf with the whiskey spirits. I'll be the old Indian spirit."

They laughed, Archibald slapping his hand on the counter, Alana's pink cheeks moving and bobbing, Elijah's shoulders heaving and swaying.

"But still," Alana's voice was serious, "I read a book about Indians and they could see things. They had ceremonies and holy places. And they communicated with the other world." Alana shivered and pulled her rabbit coat up around her shoulders.

"Well, what's so unusual about that?" Elijah wanted to know. "It's just knowin' what to say and what to do when you meet up with somebody that ain't from your part of town."

"You got that right, 'Lijah," Archibald was nodding his head emphatically. "It happen all the time in here. Sometime I wonder if what I seen ain't from another world! And what I sees, my own eyes don't believe it!" He wiped the counter with his cloth.

Alana laughed, "Well, that true, that true. Some a my customers from another planet." She turned her face to Elijah. "But still, Indians *is* special. You all *see* things."

"We only see what's there. Nothin' special about that. But we've been around for a long time. This is our home, has been for millions of years. Guess you could say we're familiar with all that's around us. Your people didn't get the chance to be familiar yet. You was brought here without your say-so. We just always been here. It's different in the city, though. I worry about the twins. They don't fish, they don't get to see the hawks. I bet some days, they don't even see the sky!" He shook his head and took another sip.

Alana grabbed Elijah's hand. "But listen, Elijah, we got falcons livin' right here in the city. I seen it on the TV. They brought these here peregrine falcons to live on a tall buildin'. And they live there, and they had babies, right there on the ledge of that buildin'. Imagine that! Those big, ole birds livin' in this city. It ain't so bad here, if you just look up." Alana smoothed her blonde curls, lit a cigarette, and sipped her drink. "It ain't so bad here."

"I saw one of them birds once," Archibald remarked. "Didn't know what the hell it was! Thought it be some kinda vulture, flyin' down on me. Like to scare me to death. It flew down and grabbed a pigeon right off the street. Right in front of me. Damn! I come into work, shakin' in my shoes, and told Alana here about it. She say it musta been one a them falcons. I was damn glad to hear it. Thought it was a messenger, bringin' me a warnin' 'bout my sinful life!" He polished the counter, making large circles in the wood.

"Don't seem to me that the spirit-keeper would have a sinful life. You look like a good man to me." Elijah squinted at Archibald. "Yeah, you look like a good man to me. That falcon was tellin' you so. It ain't everybody gets to see one. A shy bunch, those falcons. They don't mix with the rest of us."

"Aw, I don't know 'bout that," Archibald said, making larger circles with his cloth.

"Well, I do. And I says he is a good man," Alana spoke up. "He always got a drink waitin' on me when I too cold or too tired to work no more. He let me stay here, when I just *can't* go out anymore. When I had my little girl, Archibald watch her when I gotta go out and hit the street. Archibald a good man... but my baby die."

"Aw, Alana. I didn't do nothin'. I didn't do half the things I shoulda to keep you and the baby safe."

Alana waved away his protest. "You a good man. You just don't like anybody sayin' so."

Elijah touched Alana's hand. "I lost two of my babies. Only they was grown boys and they moved away. I never saw them till they came home dead. I grieve for you, Alana."

Alana's hand shook. She moved her fingers up to her eyes, surprised at the tears dropping onto the counter. "She were only a year old. She got some kinda sickness. I took her to the doctor, but he say she be alright. Just give her some aspirin. I give it to her, but the sickness don't go away. She just get worse! She die one night, in my arms. I was rockin' her and singin' to her, and she just go, like that. It were a long time ago, but it seem like it happen just last night. I'm rockin' and singin' and she die. She die. I never had me no more kids. What for? They die too." She got up and went to the jukebox. She stood there, her face hard-edged in the colored lights.

Archibald looked at Elijah. "She don't talk much about that. Hell, what's to talk about? One years old. One years old! Them doctors oughta be shot, that's what I got to say about it." He turned his back on Elijah and started to polish the glasses.

Elijah walked over to Alana and touched her face. "When they brought my boys' bodies back home, I thought I'd go crazy with all the hurt inside me. Edie never said a word. She just kissed them, then she went outside and walked. She was gone for hours. I was afraid, thought I was goin' to lose her too. But she came back. She was walkin', she said, and found a bird nest that had fallen from a tree. She climbed the tree to put the nest up in the branches. See, there was two little chicks in that nest. Ugly little things, Edie said. No feathers, just those bare little bodies and big hungry beaks. After puttin' the nest back, Edie hid and waited for the mother. She was scared the mother wouldn't come back, or if she did, she wouldn't go near 'cause Edie had touched the nest. Well, she waited and waited, and the mother came back with a mouth full of worms and fed those babies. Then Edie walked home. She said she felt better 'cause at least somewhere, there was babies that were O.K. My Edie, she was somethin'. When I saw her walkin' toward the house, my heart felt like bustin'. Just the sight of her made me think I could handle all that hurt inside me. My baby boys. They were twins, too. Never did a thing without the other one. I guess maybe it was a good thing they died together. That's what Edie said. One couldn't live without the other. I blamed myself too. Shoulda done this, shoulda done that. Just like you, Alana. But I bet you was a good mother. I can see it."

Alana lifted her head, the lights from the jukebox making patterns on her face. "I loved her, you know? She was a little angel in my life. Like a light, you know? I wish I knew that Edie. You must miss her somethin' fierce." They walked back to the counter and sat down. Archibald still had his back to them but was watching them in the mirror.

"I miss her, yes. I miss my boys. But they're still here," he pointed to his chest. "Somewhere here. And I see Edie every once in a while. She keeps an eye on me. I hear her too. She calls, *Elijah, Elijah*. That sweet voice callin'."

"I know! My Cherry Marie, she call me too! She were learnin' to talk and she say, *Mama, Mama*, all the time. I laugh at her. "Don't you know no other words?" I say to her. *Mama, Mama*. I hear that voice, my Cherry Marie callin' me. *Mama*. I hear her and I just want to follow that little voice. *Mama*."

"Don't you be followin' no voices, you hear?" Archibald whirled around and slapped his hand on the wooden surface. "You don't be followin' no voices what call you. You gotta stay here. You alive, woman, and she dead. You can't be followin' no voices." Archibald's eyes were red-rimmed and angry. "Aw, Alana, Alana." He put out his hand and touched her face. His voice became soft, "Don't follow no voices. Please, Alana."

Alana brought her hand up to Archibald's. "I won't be followin' her. I just like to hear that voice. Cherry Marie, my baby girl."

Elijah looked away from the two people. Talking about Edie, Cherry Marie, and his baby boys made him lonely, made him long for the sweet faces of the twin girls he loved so much. He felt a hand on his shoulder.

"Don't be feelin' bad, Elijah," Alana said.

"Oh, I ain't feelin' bad, just a little lonesome for my twins. But you know, it's good to talk about death. It's funny, we treat life like it ain't no big deal when it's the biggest deal there is. And we get scared to talk about death. It's just the every-day, death is. Here, have another piece of bread. When you bite into somethin' like this, you know how good life is." He handed a piece to Alana and took one for himself.

Alana took tiny bites of her bread and said, "Them twins be takin' a long time gettin' here. You need a place to stay? I got a place. It clean and warm. Shame on them girls! This here town's not a safe one. Them girls shouldn't be lettin' their grandpa be wanderin' the streets. God knows what could happen!"

"It seems pretty safe to me," Elijah smiled.

Archibald chuckled, "Well, you lucky this time."

"I think I'm pretty lucky. Meetin' you two spirits, I'd say I was a lucky man."

Feeling around in his pockets for change, Elijah announced that he'd call the twins' number again. He went to the phone booth and began dialing.

The door opened and Terrance walked in, ushering Alice and Annie into the bar.

"Grandfather!" the twins shouted and ran to hug him. "There was a terrible accident on the freeway," Alice began.

"No, no, not us," Annie reassured her grandfather.

"We didn't know what to do."

"We were so worried you'd be sitting in that bus station all alone."

"I can't tell you the thoughts that were going through..."

"My head," Annie finished.

"You tell the story, Terrance," Alice said, holding on to her grandfather and squeezing his arm.

"Well, I finished my business and went back inside the station, just like I told you I would. I'm standin' there and in walks twins, lookin' worried. I goes up to them and says, you lookin' for Elijah? They don't wanna say, not that I blames them! I told them you was across the street, waitin' on them. But they was nervous like. Can't blame them! But I finally told them what you looks like, that we play Pac-man, and you give me a piece of bread. They looked at me like I was crazy, man! Pacman? Grandfather? they say. But it were the bread what did it. They say nobody givin' away bread but Grandfather. Must be him! So they follows me over here to Al's Bar, and here we is."

Alice and Annie laughed, and Annie poked Terrance in the ribs. "Pacman! Grandpa, when did you learn to play Pacman?"

"Today."

For some reason that made the twins laugh even harder.

"Here girls, I want you to meet my friends. Alana. Archibald. We've had a good time here."

Alice and Annie shook hands with Archibald. "Pleased to meet you ladies." Their eyebrows raised only slightly at the sight of Alana while shaking her hand.

Alana said, "So these the famous twins we been hearin' 'bout all night. They're very pretty, Elijah. You must be one proud granddaddy. Girls, your granddaddy's the nicest man. But I 'spect you know that already. I'm very pleased to meet you. Such beautiful hair," and she pointed to the twins' black, shining locks.

"Thank you," said Alice. "Uh... I..."

"Think you have lovely hair too," Annie finished.

"Oh, girls, it just a wig!" Alana touched the blonde curls and looked pleased.

Archibald lay down his polishing cloth. "What'll it be ladies? Drinks on me. Anybody know 'Lijah, they welcome here anytime."

Alice and Annie looked at each other, looked at their grandfather, looked at each other again, and laughed. "We'll have a beer."

Terrance went to the jukebox and turned on the music. Koko Taylor's pounding voice came blasting out. Terrance snapped his fingers and started singing along.

"Girls, I had a dream on the bus. You were holdin' babies in your arms. They were twins, just like you."

"Oh Grandpa, we don't have any babies. At least not yet. Annie has applied, but we don't know yet."

"Well, that's why I came here. I thought I could help in gettin' you those babies. These Natives down here, they'd listen to an old man like me, now wouldn't they? I dreamed about twin babies, and I'm here to find them for you."

The twins choked a little on their drinks but smiled at their grandfather. "We'll see, Grandpa."

"Yes, we will. Now, I brought whitefish from the Bay. Hope it's still frozen. Your mother made you this fry bread. Alana calls it fry cakes. You liked it, didn't you Alana?"

Alana nodded her agreement. "Just like my grandmama used to make."

Elijah opened the sack. "There's plenty here. Just help yourself."

Terrance was the first one to dip into the bag. "Man, I been dreamin' 'bout this here fry bread since this afternoon. This is good bread!" He chewed ecstatically.

Even Archibald helped himself to a piece. "This *is* like fry cake. I'll be. You tell your mom she make good bread," he told the twins.

They assured him they would relay the message. They hugged their grandfather. "We're so glad you're here. Safe and sound."

"Why wouldn't I be?"

Elijah was very happy. Sharing food was the best thing people could do together. He was anxious to start on this adoption business, but for now, he was content to be with his friends and his twins, eating, laughing.

Outside the sign blinked off, then on. FOOD & SPIRITS. FOOD & SPIRITS. Inside there were music, stories, good food, and friends. Elijah was content.

GLOSSARY

dude   (*slang*) a man of special importance, sometimes used sarcastically
garters   elastic bands to hold up stockings

ghosts   (*slang*) men

hair stiff as a board   stiff with hair spray

hang out   (*slang*) stay in one place for a long time, not doing very much

hit the streets   work the streets (as a prostitute)

hummmpph   sound of disbelief or mild disgust

Mohawk; Six Nations   the most populous Canadian Indian band and reserve, formerly the League of the Iroquois, uniting five groups—the Seneca, Cayuga, Onondaga, Oneida and Mohawk (and later the Tuscarora)—into a single confederacy in the sixteenth century

pink spots   make-up called blush or rouge

reservation (reserve)   tracts of land set aside by the federal government which natives use but do not own

residential school   boarding schools not on the reserves, run by churches, for Indian native children to get an education similar to non-natives so that they could assimilate into non-native society

spirit place   similar to heaven, where the dead go

spirits   alcoholic drinks

turtle bolo tie   a leather tie arranged through a ring with the figure of a turtle on it

Tyendinaga   Bay of Quinte Mohawk reserve in Ontario

Vernor's   brand name of non-alcoholic ginger ale

waiting on   (*dialect of English*) waiting for

you people   Afro-American people

A CLOSER READING

1. Why does Elijah want to go to Detroit? Why is his daughter worried about his plans?

2. What does Elijah take with him to Detroit? Why do you think he does this?

3. Who does he meet first, on the bus? Where is she going? What does Elijah ask her about her hair? How do they get along?

4. What was Elijah's wife like?

5. What was Shirley's husband like?

6. What does Elijah's response about hunger tell about his background? Does Shirley hear him?

7. What are Elijah's first impressions of the city?

8. What does he refer to when he says "*Is this like TV*"?

9. What is your first impression of the young man in a Nike jacket?

10. When Terrance asks "*where you been?*" he does not expect an answer. What does he mean? Does Elijah understand him?

11. Referring to what kind of Indian his father was, Terrance says *"It's all the same."* Elijah replies *"it ain't all the same. But then again... maybe it is."* What does Terrance mean? What does Elijah mean?

12. What is the "business" Terrance has to take care of?

13. How does Archibald react to Elijah at first? How do you think Archibald got his scar?

14. Alana "hangs out" at the bar and the bus station. What does she do for a living? What does she look like? How is she dressed?

15. Elijah keeps offering people bread. He also carries whitefish. He seems very innocent. Does he remind you of someone in the Christian mythology (religion)? What does the name Elijah mean? Powless? (See *Looking at Language* below.) Do these people react to Elijah the way you think they would react to another man?

16. Why does the white man in the suit not go into the bar?

17. Alana gives her version of what Indians do. Does it sound different from what other cultures or religions do?

18. When Elijah says *"your people didn't get the chance to be familiar yet"*, what does he mean? What does he mean when he says the twins don't fish or see hawks? What do the falcons mean to Alana?

19. When Elijah tells about his twin sons dying, we are reminded of his dream on the bus. What is the connection between the two instances?

20. Is Archibald a "good man"? Explain. Why does Elijah say he can tell Alana was a "good mother"?

21. Everyone tells Elijah that Detroit is not a safe town. Do you think it is safe?

22. What does the sign FOOD & SPIRITS mean outside the bar? What does it mean in the story? Start with the denotation (definition) and then consider its connotation (all the ideas and feelings associated with "food" and "spirit").

CULTURAL DISCUSSION

1. If you had known that the story was going to be about an elderly Indian, an old lady, a drug dealer, a bartender and a prostitute, would you have had images in your mind of what they were going to be like? Would your images have been correct? Stereotypes differ among cultures. Do you think your idea of old people is the same as some Canadians' ideas?

2. Did it surprise you that the single granddaughter wanted to adopt a child? Do all societies view adoption in the same way? What about women (or men) remaining single?

3. The dialect in this story is urban Afro-American. If people hear someone speaking with an unfamiliar dialect or an accent, do they make assumptions about the person based on the way they talk?

4. Does it harm Elijah to come into contact with the people in the bar? Would it harm us? Do you know of any leaders of the world's religions who have mixed with ordinary people, including prostitutes?

5. What does Elijah say about meeting people *"that ain't from your part of town"*? How does he handle that situation in his own life?

6. Dreams are important in native culture, as the character of Elijah demonstrates. What do dreams mean to you?

7. Is the character of Elijah realistic? Is he meant to be a symbol (representing something)?

8. Is this story didactic (teaching or instructing)? If so, what does the author want to tell the reader about Indian culture? About white culture?

9. Do you (or would you) tell your children stories to teach them? To amuse them? How *do* you teach children? Should you let them freely choose their own values?

10. What is Elijah's philosophy of life? Use examples of what he says and does in the story to support your answer. Notice the sayings of Elijah and the other characters, such as *"curiosity killed the cat"*. (See also *Looking at Language*.) Do you have a philosophy of life?

LOOKING AT LANGUAGE

Cultural Sayings

A *saying* is a wise statement that is often repeated. All cultures have them. In "Food and Spirits" Elijah has many sayings which reveal his character, such as the one about *"laughter at the beginning..."* when he meets Shirley. Find several other expressions in this story and try to decide what they mean.

What do Elijah's sayings tell about Elijah's philosophy of life? Compare his sayings to the following sayings from various cultures. Remember that it is sometimes difficult to understand the sayings from a different culture.

1. If you go slowly, slowly, you will go far. (Greek)
2. With those teachers you walk, those are the lessons you will learn. (Greek)
3. If you keep a green tree in your heart, perhaps one day a singing bird will come. (Chinese)
4. Cheer up, better days are coming, even if we don't live to see them. (Irish)
5. A single line may have two hooks. (Newfoundland)
6. Empty vessels loom biggest. (Newfoundland)

Some sayings come from religion, for example, from Islam:

Knowledge is the greatest veil.
He who knows himself, knows his Lord.

or

Life is like the flame of a lamp exposed to the wind. (Buddhist)

Translate some of the expressions you have inherited. Do they tell what is most important to you?

Cultural Names

Words, and especially names, are very important in native culture. Think about Elijah Powless' name. Who was Elijah in Western culture? (Remember the influence of missionaries on native life.) Assume that the author has given the character this name on purpose. Is it an appropriate name? Why use the name "Powless" ("less" at the end of a word means the same as the word "less")? What does "pow" mean? A speaker of English might think of the sound of a punch, a pow-wow (the Indian word for a meeting or ceremony), and perhaps the word "power". Play with this name, remembering that sometimes authors are being ironic.

Do names have a significance in your first language? Explain. What about the names of birds in this story: hawk and falcon? What do they mean in this story? What do certain birds mean to different people (think of doves, for instance).

REINFORCING SKILLS

1. Traditional native literature includes features such as understatement and emotional restraint (discussed in *Looking at Language* for "The Torch Woman"). Does "Food and Spirits" use these features? Do you think the author of "Food and Spirits" has been influenced by Western traditions of story writing? Explain.

2. Is Alana being ironic when she says *"God knows what could happen"*? Is the author being ironic? Explain. (Irony was discussed after "Shun-Wai".)

ACTIVITIES

Essay Writing

1. Write an essay describing Elijah and list the effects he has on at least two characters in the story. Include why you think he has these effects.

2. Write an essay telling what Elijah's values are (cite the text). Compare his values with yours.

Summary Questions

DISCUSSIONS QUESTIONS LINKING THE STORIES

1. If the grandfather in "Lies My Father Told Me" met the grandfather in "Food and Spirits", what would they have in common?

2. As children, would the son in "A Secret Lost in the Water" have anything in common with the son in "A Penny in the Dust"? How about as adults?

3. Compare the effects of emigrating to Canada on the mother in "Shun-Wai" and the mother in "The Other Family". Do you think they would understand each other?

4. Compare the response to Cecil as a newcomer in "The Moose and the Sparrow" with the responses Elijah encounters in "Food and Spirits". How do you account for this difference?

ESSAY QUESTIONS SUMMARIZING THE TEXT

1. Family and friends is the theme of this reader. How has each story been concerned with family and/or friends? How do you think each narrator might have defined "a good family" or "a good friend"?

2. How would you define a good family or a good friend? Do they mean different things in different cultures? What do you think they mean in Canada? (This question may have several answers.)

3. The stories in this text are about legacies and adaptations. What were the legacies of the first five stories? What were the adaptations of the last five stories? Can you identify with the main characters? Would Canadians understand if you told them about your legacies and adaptations?

4. Did the picture of Canada painted in this text surprise you in any way?

5. Describe any character's actions. Could the character's actions be similar to the actions of people you grew up with?

6. Describe a character in one of the stories and tell how he or she seems like, or unlike, Canadians you have observed.

7. Give examples of customs in the area where you were born and how they show what is important to the people.

8. What is the most important thing in life to you? Compare this to the values of a character in one of the stories.

9. What do you think is the most important thing to know about Canada?

MAP OF CANADA

Settings for the Stories

Penny in the Dust, rural Nova Scotia
A Secret Lost in the Water, rural Quebec
The Torch Woman, Manitoba, near Brandon
The Dead Child, rural Manitoba
Lies My Father Told Me, Montreal
The Other Family, Toronto
Shun-Wai, Vancouver
The Moose and the Sparrow, northern British Columbia
Lifeguard, Alberta
Food and Spirits, Detroit (U.S.)